THE
ILLUSTRATED ENCYCLOPAEDIA
OF ANIMAL LIFE

THE ANIMAL KINGDOM

The strange and wonderful ways of
mammals, birds, reptiles, fishes and
insects. A new and authentic natural
history of the wild life of the world

VOLUME 7

FREDERICK DRIMMER, M.A.
EDITOR-IN-CHIEF

GEORGE G. GOODWIN
*Associate Curator of Mammals,
The American Museum of Natural
History*

CHARLES M. BOGERT
*Curator of Amphibians and Reptiles,
The American Museum of Natural
History*

DEAN AMADON
E. THOMAS GILLIARD
*Associate Curators of Birds,
The American Museum of Natural History*

CHRISTOPHER W. COATES *Curator*
JAMES W. ATZ *Assistant Curator*
*Aquarium of The New York Zoological
Society*

JOHN C. PALLISTER
Research Associate, Insects, The American Museum of Natural History

ODHAMS BOOKS LIMITED, LONG ACRE, LONDON

CARIBOU SANATORIA

Travellers to the Far North have brought back a delightful story of caribou sanatoria where the animals go to mend their broken limbs. There are those who would reject this story, calling it mere fantasy, but there is every reason to believe this tale! On several occasions, caribou have been found on secluded islands, recovering from broken limbs. They certainly could not have broken a leg on the island but must have swum there from the mainland in order to be safe from attack by wolves and other predatory beasts.

It is interesting to note, in this connection, that Nature can mend even the badly broken limbs of her children without any danger of gangrene setting in. Flies lay their eggs in the wound before a gangrenous condition develops. These hatch into maggots which devour bacteria-bearing tissue and at the same time deposit a secretion which fights infection and thereby removes the major obstacle to the animal's recovery.

SOME IMPORTANT CARIBOU

The Barren-ground Caribou, *Rangifer arcticus*, takes its name from the Barren Grounds or Barren Lands of northern Canada, where it dwells. It is very much more at home on the tundras of Alaska, too. Indeed, there, the caribou are the commonest of big game. Although these animals are given considerable protection in this region, they seem to be moving farther north in their search for conditions promising more insurance against slaughter.

Usually the antlers of the Barren Ground caribou are very long and slender, and with several points projecting from the flattened tips.

Here are some distinctive features that they have in common with other caribou:

The cloven hoofs are usually broad and wide-spreading, and attached to them are dewclaws—small vestiges of hoofs (sometimes called "false hoofs") that are of some value on snow-covered terrain. The nose is covered with hair—an excellent protection against extreme cold.

Caribou are usually brown, paler and greyer on the back and darker on the legs and head. The neck and the throat are white or whitish. There is considerable variation in height among these beasts

—they stand anywhere from forty to sixty inches at the shoulder. The disparity in weight is even more striking; some caribou have been found weighing as little as two hundred pounds, others as much as seven hundred.

Rutting time for the Barren Ground caribou is in September and October, at the height of migration. The big-eyed, dappled fawns are born on the Arctic tundra during the seemingly endless "day" of June when every bank is a bed of gay spring flowers.

We have seen how abundant caribou once were, and have noted that they are as good as extinct in the United States. It is no exaggeration to say that the animal owes its continued existence today to the remoteness of its homeland. The caribou's habit of travelling in the open and its rather poor eyesight make it an easy prey for the hunter and the wolf.

THE REINDEER'S WILD BROTHER

To the Eskimos and northern Indians, the caribou is the staff of life: it provides choice meat, hide for clothing, and bones for weapons. A caribou with a broken limb, it is said, has the amazing ingenuity to withdraw to a sheltered island, away from the mainland where wolves would attack it. Here it remains till it is fit again. Pictured above is the woodland caribou, native to the north-eastern United States and Canada.

There are several varieties of Barren Ground caribou, including the Greenland Caribou. A small, light-coloured beast with slender antlers, it represents food, clothing, and shelter for many hardy people that live in desolate, frozen Greenland. The Dwarf Caribou of Queen Charlotte Island is a midget, comparatively speaking, as it stands no more than thirty-three inches high at the shoulder.

The Woodland Caribou, *Rangifer caribou,* is darker and more heavily built than the Barren Ground caribou. The antlers, though less spreading, are stouter and more flattened. These deer are found through the forests from the extreme north-eastern tip of the United States to Great Slave Lake in Canada and Newfoundland. Related animals dwell in the Canadian Rockies and the Pacific coast region.

The Old World Caribou, or Reindeer, *Rangifer tarandus,* and its relatives, once roamed from the Scandinavian peninsula eastward across Europe and through Siberia. Today they have almost disappeared in the wild everywhere but in the Siberian part of their ancient domain. However, these animals are still common in domesticated herds, as "reindeer".

THE "REINDEER AGE"

Wild or domesticated, reindeer or caribou have had an amazingly long association with man. It was the "Reindeer Age" that marked the dawn of human history.

In that period—it was twenty-five thousand to thirty thousand years ago—there were made, on cave walls, the first pictures that have come down to us. The artists, the "Reindeer Men" of the late Old Stone Age, left wonderful likenesses of contemporary animals—birds, snakes, horses, elephants, bears, bison, ibex, and oxen. But the best pictures of all were those of the reindeer—the most numerous big game in Europe and the principal support of man in that age.

REINDEER AND MAN

Just when was the reindeer first domesticated? There has been a great deal of dispute on the subject, but our earliest reference to a domesticated reindeer seems to be from a Chinese source dated A.D. 499.

It would appear that domestication was very tardy, if we are to judge from the fact that neither the Eskimo nor the Indian made any attempt to tame this animal, which was so common in northern America. Domesticated reindeer, to be sure, have for a long time played an important part in the lives of the Tungus and Chukchi tribes in eastern Siberia. The animal is bred for riding, harnessed to sledges, and used for food. The Lapps and their Scandinavian neighbours milk their reindeer, churn butter, and make cheese from it.

Domesticated reindeer did not make their appearance in America until 1892, when 162 Siberian animals were landed at Teller, Alaska, for the benefit of hungry Indians and Eskimos. During the following decade, 1,118 more Siberian reindeer were transported to the shore of St. Clarence Bay. Well over a hundred thousand of the descendants of these imported animals have been killed for food and clothing.

REINDEER IN LAPLAND

Norway, Sweden, and Finland are reindeer countries, and the Lapps who live in the northern regions of those lands, are staunch admirers of the great antlered creatures. Their philosophy is that the reindeer is more important than they are—the animals can get along without them, but they cannot get along without the reindeer.

The Lapps do not drive their deer, like other herdsmen. Nomads, they follow the herds from the summer feeding grounds to the winter ones, and draw their living from the beasts.

The reindeer is food, clothing, and transportation to these folk of the Far North. The hair is used by the Lapps to stuff mattresses; the hides are made into parkas, gloves, trousers, and shoes; the sinew is used for thread; and the stomach membranes come in handy as food containers and for packing cheese made from reindeer milk. Reindeer milk, by the way, is about four times as rich in butter fat as cow's milk, and a few drops will turn coffee white.

A reindeer team, pulling a sledge, is a strange sight to those who have not seen it before; the Lapps harness up to nine or ten reindeer in single file to their sleds, each animal being tied to the one ahead by the reins. A single reindeer, as a beast of burden, can carry a load of ninety pounds. It can pull 450 pounds and travel forty miles a day. Of course this cannot be a continuous operation—the animal must have time to rest and feed.

Reindeer prefer to travel into the wind even in the face of a bitter

Arctic storm. When rounded up, they all mill around in one direction, either clockwise or counter-clockwise. A spectacle not easily forgotten is a sea of their horns whirling.

A FANTASTIC TREK

One of the greatest examples of human and animal endurance is found in the story of the great trek of Dan Crowley and Andrew Bahr. These men undertook to drive a herd of three thousand reindeer from the Selawik River in Alaska to Kittigazuit across the Mackenzie delta in Canada. On Christmas Day, 1929, the expedition started the long trek in the dim glow of the Arctic light and headed north.

The distance Crowley and Bahr had to cover was actually no more than one thousand miles. But it was a thousand miles of unexplored wilderness—of snow-swept tundra and dangerous mountain passes. For months at a time, the men were lost and out of touch with civilization, which supposed that the entire outfit had perished from hunger and privation. Finally, the hardy travellers reached their destination. They had expected to make the trip in eighteen months; instead, it actually took them five years and two months!

How did the reindeer survive the journey? Crowley and Bahr delivered 2,370 animals in Kittigazuit. Only 10 per cent of these had been in the original herd that had left Alaska. The rest of that group had perished or been lost, but their places had been taken by youngsters born during the five-year trek.

ROE DEER—RACERS AND JUMPERS

The Roe Deer, *Capreolus*, is one of the smartest looking of the smaller deer of Europe and Asia. A pert, compact, and sturdy animal, its fleet figure may be glimpsed flashing through forest glades, especially in the mountains.

This alert woodland creature is an excellent high jumper; it is particularly graceful as it springs over tall ferns and heather. On even ground it swings along with an easy canter, head held high. When pursued, it often pauses to listen and look back, and is loath to leave cover. It can climb rocky cliffs with the agility of a chamois.

Though they are not sociable by nature, several roe deer may occupy a small area of woodland; it is not unusual for groups of three or four to feed together. During the autumn these animals tend to migrate from one feeding ground to another. and in Manchuria from three hundred to five hundred roe deer have been seen on the march together.

Perhaps it is some obscure and half-forgotten mating ritual, or just pure playfulness, that impels roe deer to gather in certain localities where they gambol round and round after each other, wearing a circular track on the forest floor.

The doe brings forth her young in June, some forty weeks after mating. The fawns, usually twins, are marked with three rows of white spots on their tawny coats. The doe is very affectionate toward her babies and cannot stay far away when they are in danger. She is always on the lookout to protect her fawns or lead them to safety when enemies such as the fox or the golden eagle appear.

Roe deer stand from twenty-six to thirty-four inches at the shoulder and weigh about sixty pounds. Their horns are small (thirteen to sixteen inches long) and they rise abruptly together from the top of the head. The beam is very rough at the base, branching into a short forward prong and a longer rear tine that is forked at the tip.

Thick, harsh hair, brownish yellow in summer but duller brown in winter, covers the animal's body, while a bright white patch sets off the rump and stubby tail. The roe deer has a loud, sharp bark, something like that of a collie dog.

We meet the roe deer throughout Europe and across to the Pacific coast of northern Asia.

The Giraffe Family—
Not All Are Skyscrapers

ONE OF the most amazing sights to be seen on the African veldt is a herd of giraffes moving at full gallop along the skyline. They travel with marvellous grace of form and rhythm of action.

Next to the trees the giraffes are the tallest living things on earth. Some of these beautiful, slender creatures are over nineteen feet high, and eighteen feet is not exceptional at all. The giraffe's shoulder height of twelve feet is rarely surpassed even by an elephant; and a man can actually stand upright between a giraffe's front legs.

In open country this animal can speed along at thirty-two miles per hour.

But even when it comes to the bush, the tall giraffe is still at no disadvantage—it does not need to slacken its speed. Instead, it swings along, swaying its head and long neck under the branches and in between the trees, without any danger of a crash.

Perhaps one of the reasons the giraffe swings along so gracefully is that when travelling it usually paces like a camel; the legs on the same side of the body move simultaneously. This produces an even, swaying motion akin to the roll of a ship riding the waves. Of course, the giraffe also walks, trots, and canters, as well as gallops.

Another trait that the giraffe has in common with the camel is that it does not show to advantage in the water. It is a poor wader, and is unable to swim. A deep river is an impassable barrier as far as the giraffe is concerned.

Dry, arid country, where the ground is packed firm and hard, is essential for the giraffe. In deep mud and swampy country it will bog down and become hopelessly mired. Even though its hoofs may measure twelve inches in length, they cannot support the huge, tall body on anything but solid ground.

GIRAFFES OF THE PAST

The giraffe's ancestors roamed Asia and Europe in primitive times, but they never reached America. In recent times, the modern giraffe has lived exclusively on African soil.

Europeans of long ago, having never seen a giraffe, thought of it as a legendary creature rather than a living animal. Its name comes from the Arab *zarafa*, with the twofold meaning: "a creature of grace", and "one who walks swiftly". In South Africa it was known as the *kameel*, and to the early Romans it was the *camelopardalis*, a mythical creature with a leopard for its father and a camel for its mother. The first giraffe to reach Europe was imported by Julius Caesar, who exhibited it in Rome in 46 B.C.

KINDS OF GIRAFFES

There are two very distinct types of giraffes. The common species found over most of Africa south of the Sahara is generally referred to as the Blotched Giraffe, *Giraffa camelopardalis*. There are eleven named local variations of the common giraffe. The Reticulated or Netted Giraffe, *Giraffa reticulata*, is the other, and more handsome, variety; we find it in East Africa. This creature has large, four-sided, liver-coloured spots separated by a sharply defined network of narrow white lines.

A BIG, ATTRACTIVE CREATURE

Apart from being the tallest animal in the world, the giraffe comes close to being the third biggest in bulk, competing with the rhino for this honour. A large bull giraffe weighs two tons. A cow is two or three feet shorter than her mate, and weighs about twelve hundred pounds.

Almost as remarkable as the length of the giraffe's neck is the fact that it has no more bones in its neck than has a horse or a cow. The length of the neck is due entirely to the elongation of the bones—not to any extra vertebrae.

The shoulders of a giraffe are, of course, much higher than the hindquarters.

Both male and female giraffes have horns—quite short ones, covered with skin and hair, and tufted with black at the tip. Some giraffes of the northern species have a third horn, between the eyes, in front of the usual pair on the forehead.

Not only that, but old bulls often have a rudimentary second pair. These are in the form of low bosses, and are placed behind the first pair.

The giraffe's large, dark-brown eyes, shaded by long black lashes, have a soulful, appealing expression. The giraffe has the keenest sight of any game animal in Africa; naturally its height allows it to command an extensive view.

A giraffe's lips are long, hairy, and prehensile. The long, extendible tongue measures up to eighteen inches in the adult. The neck is maned with short hair, while the comparatively long tail has a tuft of hair at the tip.

FRIENDS AND ENEMIES

Though the giraffe is a sociable creature, the herds are never large. Rarely do we find more than ten or fifteen giraffes together. These herds are cows with their calves and usually only one full-grown bull. Bulls that do not have a harem live alone or go about in twos or threes.

LONGEST NECK IN THE WORLD

The giraffe is the tallest animal on earth—a large bull may stand nineteen feet high. In the wilder parts of Africa the animal is cautious and shy, but in tourist-frequented regions it becomes remarkably tame and sure of itself. Its main enemy, besides man, is the lion.

A dangerous foe if put to the test, the giraffe can strike a smashing blow with its head, or deliver a terrific kick with its fore and hind feet. The customary first attack is with the head.

BULL FIGHTS

In a duel between two bulls, each animal strikes for the chest and neck. Occasionally one giraffe will miss its mark and hit the ground with a resounding thud. However, these thumping combats rarely have a fatal ending. True, a really well-placed blow from a hundred-pound head could conceivably break the opponent's neck. Giraffes have been seen with dislocated neckbones, and dead bulls have been found with a broken neck—probably the result of these battles.

A giraffe's horns are hardly serious weapons. Rounded and padded at the tip, they do not penetrate. Apart from relying on head blows, the giraffe makes good use of its forefeet when fighting ordinary foes. We have spoken of its "terrific kick"—remember that it is backed up by well over a ton of bone and muscle.

THE GIRAFFE'S MORTAL ENEMY

Apart from its own kind—and, of course, man—the giraffe has only one natural enemy in Africa: the lion. Even this dangerous assailant will attack only under certain conditions. First, the big cat must be pressed by hunger. Second, a single lion would not undertake to attack a full-grown giraffe; but two or more lions have been known to kill a mature bull. Finally, lions will strike only when the giraffe is vulnerable—when reaching down to drink. At such times, the giraffe has to spread the forelegs wide apart before its mouth can reach the water level.

The giraffe has a fairly long life expectancy; it has lived in captivity for twenty-eight years.

THE HARMLESS GIRAFFE

We can say of the giraffe that its character is blameless. It never hurts anyone or anything unless in defence of its life. Nor is it a menace to farmers or their interests in any way. Once in a while, however, it may prove a nuisance. Thus, in Uganda some years ago, six hundred miles of telegraph line went out of commission; four or five giraffes had run into the wires, nearly decapitating themselves. By raising the line to thirty feet, officials avoided further trouble.

The giraffe is fond of dry and open brush country; deep forest and swampy land are equally distasteful to this skyscraping creature. Trees are more or less essential for its livelihood, since it cannot graze on the ground, except with difficulty. Leaves and shoots of the acacia, the most common tree of the African veldt, are this animal's favourite food. And it is important to remember that against a background of acacia trees the markings on a giraffe resemble blotches of shadow and light—ideal camouflage for this tall animal.

The giraffe can do without water for quite a while—several weeks, even a month. Its ability to get moisture from leaves explains why it is sometimes found in the driest country, miles from water. Where water is readily available, it drinks regularly. A giraffe will drink about two gallons a week.

Even such a simple matter as sleeping becomes quite a problem for an animal with the giraffe's outsize height. Some grown giraffes (like some elephants) rarely lie down; they prefer to sleep standing up. They have found that all the bother of lying down and getting up again simply involves too much effort. This custom is not always strictly followed; in some regions, giraffes habitually lie down to sleep.

MUTE OR VOCAL?

There is a popular belief that the giraffe has no vocal cords and is therefore mute. The same is thought of a number of other animals— possibly because no one has happened to be around when they were exercising their vocal powers. In any event, the giraffe is not voiceless —we have evidence of its uttering sounds. For example, a cow giraffe will produce a low call-note when her calf strays out of bounds. In at least one case, a calf giraffe, ridden down on horseback, "blared" like a steer.

When Dr. Goss, veterinarian at the New York Zoological Park, performed a post-portem on a large bull giraffe, he found only undeveloped vocal cords. Yet this animal had uttered several groans or moos before dying! We may therefore say that the giraffe possesses ineffective vocal cords, but it can make sounds without them.

JUNIOR GIRAFFES

Giraffes seem to have no fixed mating season. The newborn calf, which arrives fourteen or fifteen months after the mating, is a mere five and one-half feet high. An ungainly little creature, it is all neck and legs.

Somewhat wobbly at first, a baby giraffe can stand and move around under its own power twenty minutes after birth, and is all ready for its first meal. While nursing during the early stages, the calf braces itself between the mother's forelegs. For the first nine months, the calf is dependent on its mother's milk. After this it is tall enough to reach the branches of the acacia tree and feed itself.

Like all other young creatures, the baby giraffe loves to play and frolic. In a herd where there are several calves in the kindergarten stage, they are supervised by two or three watchful guardians. It is the grown-ups' duty to keep the youngsters from straying too far afield where they might be an easy prey for lions. If the frolicking of an overdaring youngster takes it out of bounds, one of the guardians will gallop off to bring it back into the fold.

THE MYSTERIOUS OKAPI

In natural history books published before 1900 there is no mention of the okapi—the animal was not known to the white man before that date.

Many years ago pygmies living in the dense forest of the Congo told of a strange, elusive creature inhabiting their country. They described it as being built like a giraffe, striped like a zebra, and with large ears like a donkey. Hunters and explorers who visited these remote jungles, where tangled vines and dense forest growth blot out the sun for miles and miles, could never even get a glimpse of these seemingly mythical creatures.

Finally, the little brown people produced a skin of the animal. Here was tangible proof that what they had been speaking of was no phantom of the imagination. The white man's curiosity was now thoroughly aroused and his reputation as a scientist was at stake. What would the animal prove to be? Some kind of a horse, was the first guess—or perhaps an antelope.

But the suppositions were all wrong. The animal turned out to be more closely related to the giraffe than to any other living animal. The little brown men were vindicated—as anyone who had had dealings with the pygmies should have expected they would be.

GIRAFFES AND OKAPIS

The earliest giraffes, which lived about fifteen million years ago, were the common ancestors of our modern giraffe and okapi. Today both of these creatures are grouped in the family Giraffidae, even though the okapi's neck is nowhere near as long as the giraffe's.

The relatively short-necked okapi is the "normal" member of the giraffe family. The primitive giraffes of millions of years ago—we call them "palaetragines"—looked very much like the okapi of today, resembling it in size and general structure. It is the elongated skyward animal—the typical giraffe—that is the oddity of the family. Through the ages the giraffe developed a longer and longer neck, becoming more and more unlike its ancestors. The okapi, on the other hand, advanced along a conventional course, following conservative lines in its development.

THE GIRAFFE'S SMALL COUSIN
Although the okapi is a fairly familiar sight in zoos, where it quickly makes itself at home, this creature of the dense African forests was almost unknown to science before 1900. A peculiar-looking animal, the okapi has a shorter neck than its close relative the giraffe, and is smaller than an ox in size; stripes on its upper legs add to its strangeness.

THE DISCOVERY OF THE OKAPI

For years, as we have seen, this strange mule-like animal was known only to the forest pygmies of Africa. The first rumours of its existence that were to receive serious attention came to the famous journalist and explorer Henry M. Stanley. He passed on the story to Sir Harry Johnston, at that time governor of Uganda. In 1899 Sir Harry obtained a few scraps of skin of the mysterious animal from the natives. He sent on the evidence to Dr. P. L. Sclater in London, who conjectured that they might belong to a hitherto unknown variety of zebra.

Two years later Sir Harry secured a complete skin and two skulls of this legendary creature—the only large animal that had escaped the notice of science until the twentieth century. The discovery created a furore among zoologists throughout the world. Dr. Sclater named the animal *Okapia johnstoni*, in honour of the governor. It was not until 3 August, 1937, that the first living okapi to reach American shores arrived at the New York Zoological Park.

THE OKAPI AT HOME

The okapi lives in deep forest country, yet its vision is not very well suited for the dim light that filters through the dense vegetation of its favourite surroundings. Luckily, its keen senses of smell and hearing compensate for this failing.

When disturbed, the okapi gallops away, carrying its head forward in line with the body; it can keep up a fast pace for long distances. A leaf-eater, the okapi browses on forest trees. It is often solitary, though sometimes two may be seen together. The single baby is built like the adult and has the same unusual colouring.

The okapi's colour is distinctive, with the body and neck a rich dark-brown, and the head buffy white. The markings on the hindquarters are unique—slantwise stripes of black and white. The lower limbs are white with a narrow black band. The comparatively long tail ends in a tuft of hair.

Resemblances to the Giraffe. The okapi's tongue, like the giraffe's, is extendible, and the lips—again like the giraffe's—are prehensile. Thus the tongue and lips are adapted for picking foliage. There are also resemblances between the two animals in the teeth. The feet are of the regular even-toed hoofed-mammal type.

Although the okapi's limbs and neck are relatively long, they have none of the exaggerated qualities typical of the giraffe. The body is short and compact, and the hind limbs give a deceptive impression of being much longer than the front limbs. The male okapi stands a bit over five feet at the shoulder; the female is smaller.

The Okapi's Horns. One of the most striking resemblances of the okapi to the giraffe is found in the horns. In the okapi, they have a maximum length of five inches, and are covered for most of their length by hair. Unlike the horns and antlers of deer and antelope, the okapi's horns do not grow out from the skull. Actually they are independent of the skull before birth, being within the flesh; later on they grow downwards and become firmly fused to the skull. This is also true of the horns of the typical giraffes.

The okapi's favourite haunts, so far as we know, are in the Semliki and Ituri forests of the upper Congo in the African Equatorial zone.

Pronghorns—America's Swiftest Runners

IN THE early pioneering days of America, the pronghorn was as much a part of the West as the buffalo, the Indian, and the prairie dog. Natural enemies may have taken a limited toll of its numbers, and the Indians—still without horses in those days—no doubt killed a few pronghorns with bow and arrow. Still, when the white man arrived, the pronghorn teemed on the western plains in herds of many thousands.

Of all the living hoofed mammals, the pronghorn is among the few—possibly the only one—whose ancestors were American and did not emigrate from the Old World in remote ages. The original pronghorn country extended from the southern junction of Saskatchewan and Alberta in Canada, through the region south-west of the Mississippi valley, to central Mexico. Today we find the animal only in a few parts of the upland plains in the Rocky Mountain area.

REMARKABLE HORNS

The pronghorn is distinctive, above all, for its unique horns. Like the horns of sheep, goats, and antelope, they are hollow and composed of a sheath that covers a bony core. Despite this similarity, the pronghorn's horns are different in two ways.

One difference is that the horns of this animal are pronged (hence its name). None of the other hollow-horned hoofed mammals have this feature. We might accept this branching of the horns as a reasonable variation of the hollow-horned group if it were not for the second remarkable difference; while the others keep their horns for life, the pronghorn sheds its horny sheath every year.

The entire outside sheath is eased off the bony core by the formation of the new horn underneath, and is shed in the autumn soon after the rutting season has ended. The new sheath begins to grow from the tip of the core, and spreads slowly downwards until it reaches the base. During the time it is growing, it is covered with skin and hair, which are lost when the horn matures and hardens. Both bucks and does have horns, but the females have smaller and more slender ones than the males. In fact, some does lack horns altogether.

THE PRONGHORN'S WARNING SIGNAL

Most animals have some means of communicating with their fellows. This is especially true of the social creatures that live in herds. The pronghorn's signal is one of the most remarkable pieces of Nature's handiwork—it is quite silent.

This is how it works. The hairs on the animal's rump are white and longer than those found anywhere else on the body. The roots are embedded in special muscular sheaths, which make it possible for the pronghorn to erect the rump hairs at will in the shape of a great rosette.

When the animal raises this white rosette or shield, it reflects an incredible amount of light. The shield is especially brilliant if flashed in the bright sunlight, and can be seen from a distance of nearly four miles.

When it senses danger, the pronghorn transmits its fears by this flashing signal, thus alerting the pronghorns and other animals in its vicinity. The pronghorn usually travels without making a sound.

STRANGE SIGHT—A SEA OF REINDEER ANTLERS
Reindeer are unlike other members of the deer family in that both sexes possess antlers. They are the most sociable of deer—migrating herds numbering thousands have been seen in northern Canada. Here their deadliest natural enemy is the Arctic wolf, but they can generally escape him by running, if not taken unawares. Reindeer are at home in both the Old World and the New; in the latter region they are generally known as caribou. *See page 743.*

LONGEST NECK ON EARTH

The giraffe, which sometimes grows to a height of nineteen feet, finds its long neck a great convenience in reaching the top branches of trees for the leaves on which it feeds. When it drinks, the situation is different; the animal must spread its forelimbs far apart and bend its knees in order to reach the water. In dry seasons it may go for a month without drinking. *See page 752.*

A FAMILY ALL BY ITSELF

It is true that we often refer to the Pronghorn, *Antilocapra americana*, as the pronghorn "antelope", and that in a general way it does resemble an antelope. Yet the pronghorn is not an antelope. It shows certain traits of deer and cattle, but, for all that, it does not belong to either of these families, nor is it closely related to any other group of animals found under the heading of even-toed hoofed mammals. And so scientists have had to allot the pronghorn a family all to itself, the Antilocapridae.

THE MUCH-HUNTED PRONGHORN

Wild-life experts estimate that North America was once the home of forty million pronghorns; today, only a few hundred thousand of these handsome, harmless, antelope-like creatures remain in the American Far West. Pronghorns are fleet of foot, but they are also possessed of great curiosity, and so they are easy victims for the man with the gun.

AN INSULATED COAT

Living as it does on the great open spaces, where there is no shelter from bitter winter winds, the pronghorn has a special insulated coat that helps to conserve body heat. This covering is made up of long, tightly packed hair, full and deep. Each hair is a hollow tube filled with a pithlike substance. A rich reddish brown or tan, the coat is darkened on the mane along the neck with blackish brown.

The pronghorn is medium sized, as animals go. Grown bucks measure thirty-two to forty inches at the shoulder, and weigh from one hundred to 125 pounds; females average 10 per cent smaller in size and weight. Specially adapted for travel over hard, arid plains and upland plateaus, the pronghorn, unlike most other ruminants, has no small "extra" hoofs (dewclaws) on the back of its foot.

With a top speed of nearly a mile a minute, the pronghorn is the swiftest runner in America. In fact, in the whole world it may rank second, next to the cheetah of India.

Pronghorn dry does (does that have borne no young), by the way, are fleeter than the bucks.

PRONGHORN ENEMIES

Though the coyote, wolf, cougar, and eagle are among the pronghorn's natural enemies, snow is its most dreaded foe of all. Deep snow deprives the pronghorn of its natural food supply—grasses, brush, and the like. Moreover, it causes the animal to founder as it attempts to forage. At the same time, the deep snow drives the wolves and coyotes frantic with hunger.

During excessively cold and snowy winters, pronghorns starve to death by the thousands. During the fearful winter of 1893, when the temperature fell to 61° below zero at Fort Assiniboine, Montana, nine hundred antelope perished in the deep drifts near the post.

PRONGHORN MATING AND THE YOUNG

Pronghorns mate in the autumn, usually in September. During the rutting season, the larger bands split up into small groups—generally a buck with three or four does. Like the males of most of the deer family, the mating pronghorn bucks are truculent and savage, fighting fierce battles for possession of the does. Once the rut is over, all live peacefully together.

About eight months after the mating season, late in May or early June, twin fawns or, occasionally, triplets are born. Baby pronghorns develop fast. When only a few days old, they can dash away at twenty-five miles an hour.

Hiding is the best precaution against danger, as far as the little ones are concerned. The wise old mother stations her twins about a hundred yards apart, remaining away herself except at nursing time, and they lie hidden in the tall grass until her return. She is seldom far off, and keeps a watchful eye open for a prowling coyote or a hunting eagle; if such an enemy appears, she will try to lure it away, distracting its attention from her young.

Despite the extensive hunting of the past, these animals, aided by conservation policies, seem to be holding their own. In recent years, the pronghorn population has come close to three hundred thousand.

Buffaloes, Wild Cattle, Yaks, and Other Oxen

THE OXEN, or cattle, are the most important members of the animal kingdom so far as man is concerned, for they supply him with meat and milk in great quantity. You will search in vain among these beasts for a purple cow:

> *I never saw a purple cow,*
> *I never hope to see one;*
> *But I can tell you anyhow,*
> *I'd rather see than be one.*

That animal appears to have been thought of for the first time around the turn of the century (1897) by an American writer of light verses, Gelett Burgess. But other kinds of cows and cattle there are in abundance, and many, especially in the wild, are fascinating creatures.

The Egyptians and Babylonians were among the early peoples that used oxen for their needs. They milked their cows as early as 3,000 B.C. However, man kept oxen long before the Egyptian civilization arose; he may have used them originally for sacrificial purposes. The ancient Chinese harnessed the oxen as beasts of burden, but they never milked any of their female animals.

CATTLE FOR THE NEW WORLD

In olden times, the Spaniards were noted for their cattle and for their passionate interest in bull fighting, a sport that goes back to the ancient Cretans. Columbus, on his second voyage in 1493, seems to have brought the first cattle to America. However, the first reliable record we have is of a number of calves from Santo Domingo, which were landed near Veracruz, Mexico, in 1521.

The Texas longhorn, once so popular in the southern United States and Mexico, originated from a type found in Spain during the fifteenth and sixteenth centuries. This animal's horns are so long that it is not easily transported. After 1860, the Hereford rapidly—and completely—replaced the Texas longhorns on American ranges. Herefords are red cattle with white faces and long horns. When grass of good quality is available, they are soon fattened and ready for market.

(Incidentally, Texas probably holds the world's record for the largest domestic ox—an animal that weighed over twenty-eight hundred pounds.)

SOME FAMED BREEDS OF CATTLE

Though the domestication of cattle goes back thousands of years, it is only in comparatively recent times that man has achieved miraculous results by selective breeding. Consider, for example, the Jersey cow, which yields over five thousand pounds of milk of the finest quality in the course of a single year. Even more remarkable, perhaps, is the Holstein variety, so productive that it furnishes its own weight in milk in two weeks.

No less noteworthy have been the results achieved in breeding cattle for their meat. Apart from the Hereford, which we have already mentioned, there are such notable breeds as the Shorthorn (which also produces abundant milk) and Aberdeen Angus.

THE FAMILY OF THE OXEN

Although, from the human standpoint, the oxen are the most valuable members of their family (Bovidae), that family includes other groups of animals that are of the greatest economic importance to us.

There are, for example, the goats and sheep. The domestication of these two animals goes back some five thousand years; for much of that time, people all over the world have been dependent on them for food and clothing.

The antelopes, limited to Africa and Asia, make up a fourth group. They are handsome creatures, still in the wild state with one or two minor exceptions; they are favourite game animals.

Finally, the family Bovidae includes the goat antelopes, animals that live in almost inaccessible mountain regions. As their name indicates, they share some of the characteristics which we associate with goats and antelopes.

For the most part, the Bovidae are an Old World family, well represented in Asia and Africa and only moderately so in Europe. No members of the family are native to South America, Australia, or Madagascar.

North America has only a few Bovidae, but they are spectacular beasts—the musk ox, the almost legendary bison, the Rocky Mountain goat, and the bighorn sheep.

A word about the Bovidae in general. They all have cloven hoofs—that is, they are even-toed. They are ruminants, or cud-chewers. All have permanent horns, simple and unbranched. These consist of a hollow horny sheath growing over pointed bony cores that arise from the front of the skull. (American frontiersmen used to separate the sheath from the core and use the former as a powder horn.) The horns continue to grow throughout the life of the animal and are never shed. Always occurring in pairs, the horns are often—though not always—present in both sexes.

We turn back now to the first group of this great family, the wild oxen.

WILD ANCESTOR OF OUR CATTLE

The tame cattle of today are descended from wild ancestors. One of the most interesting was the Aurochs, or Urus, *Bos taurus primigenius*, once found in many parts of Europe and in northern Africa from

Egypt to Morocco and Algeria. This large beast—it stood six feet at the shoulder—had disappeared in Britain before the arrival of the Romans (who elsewhere referred to it as *Bos urus*), and became extinct as a wild animal early in the sixteenth century; the last known specimen died in Poland in 1627. The aurochs was once plentiful in Palestine; it appears to be mentioned in the Bible as the "unicorn".

WILD OX OF THE ANCIENT WORLD

The aurochs or urus, ancestor of our present-day domestic cattle, once roamed much of Europe and northern Africa. Well known to the ancient Israelites, the aurochs is mentioned in the text of the Old Testament several times. This creature is now extinct—the last aurochs appears to have died in 1627. (Its name is sometimes applied to the wisent, or European bison, an entirely different animal.)

WATER BUFFALOES

A tremendous fellow, the Asiatic Buffalo, Carabao, or Water Buffalo, *Bubalus bubalis*, fears no living thing in its native jungle. There have been occasions where a water buffalo disputed the right of way with an elephant! Even the huge rhinoceros is more discreet—at least in respect to challenging an elephant's right of way.

Savage and unreliable in disposition, especially when aroused, the water buffalo is an extremely dangerous animal to stalk. This is due in some measure to the dense cover in which it is found, but even more to the fact that this behemoth has comparatively little fear of man and seems to be able to sense when it is being followed. It will take the offensive against a tiger, and—what is still more impressive —it is capable of besting the big cat in a duel. Like the tiger, the water buffalo is hunted in India from the back of an elephant.

STARTLING DOCILITY OF TAME WATER BUFFALOES

Bred in captivity, the water buffalo is very different from its wild relatives. The domesticated animals are so gentle that they can be driven in herds by native children. What makes the contrast in disposition even more amazing is that you generally cannot tell the wild from the domesticated varieties, as far as mere appearance is concerned.

We find the domesticated buffaloes all the way from Egypt to India and the Philippines. (The Borneo Buffalo, a smaller-horned cousin, dwells in the river valleys of north-east Borneo). The taming of the water buffalo goes back to at least 3,000 B.C. From then on, it was introduced in many of the warmer parts of the Old World.

Although the water buffalo's milk has a high butter-fat content, the animal is not so important as a dairy animal, since its supply of milk is rather scanty. On the other hand, the cowlike tractability and docility of the domesticated buffaloes qualify them as useful draught animals, and they have been pullers of ploughs and carts since ancient times.

HUGE AND POWERFUL

The huge water buffalo exceeds all the oxen in size—a large bull stands five feet at the shoulder. As for the horns, they are the largest in the whole Bovidae family. The shape of these horns varies somewhat. The typical ones are rough and flattened, sweeping out from the sides of the head in a wide arc. However, some water buffaloes have horns that are nearly straight at the base and turn up only near the tips. Measured along the curve, the greatest recorded length for the horns of this species is a trifle over seventy-seven inches.

Heavily built, this powerful animal has stout legs and a long tail ending in a brush of stiff hairs, that serve as a fly-swatter. The muzzle is large and square, the head is carried low. Scantily haired, the water buffalo's hide is dark ashy-grey, almost black, in colour.

THE UNTAMED WATER BUFFALO LOOKS DECEPTIVELY PEACEFUL

Seen standing in its favourite spot, a waterhole—hidden among tall grasses—the Asiatic buffalo or carabao looks like a docile if not sluggish animal. Yet it will on occasion pit itself against even the lordly elephant and the savage tiger. It shows little fear of man. Domesticated, the water buffalo is a marvel of meekness and reliability.

The water buffalo, as we might gather from its name, loves the water and is never so happy as when it is wallowing in a soft mud-hole. Here it will stay for hours during the heat of the day, with only its eyes and nostrils exposed, blissfully softening its thick hide in the ooze. In the water it is safe from torment by the hordes of biting fleas and other insect pests.

BULLS AND COWS

Old bulls are usually solitary, having their own particular home territory and guarding it zealously against all newcomers. In general, however, cows and their calves associate with a bull in herds of various sizes.

Cows have one or two young at a time during the summer, ten months after mating.

We still find the water buffalo in the wild state in north-eastern India, Ceylon, and parts of Indo-China and the Malay Peninsula. It favours tall-grass country and reed beds that border watercourses and swampland.

SOME ISLAND BUFFALOES

The Tamarao, or Philippine Pygmy Buffalo, is a small buffalo of the southern Philippine Islands. Its short, stout horns are about twenty inches long. Frequenting thickets and marshes along watercourses, it also dwells in bamboo forests in the mountains up to altitudes of six thousand feet.

The Celebes Anoa, or Pygmy Buffalo, is the smallest of the wild cattle. It has shorter and straighter horns than the tamarao—they rarely reach a length of fifteen inches. We are told that the Celebes Anoa lives alone or in pairs, frequenting the wooded mountain slopes in the Celebes.

SACRED CATTLE

The Zebu or Humped Cattle of India, *Bos indicus*, are held sacred in their native land—especially by the Brahmins. Following the tenets of Hindu faith, the bull is dedicated to Brahma, the Supreme Creator. When branded with the mark of Siva, the four-handed deity of destruction, this bull is allowed to wander where it pleases. No Hindu would dare object, even should it take a fancy to the vegetables in his garden or even in his shop. (Some monkeys enjoy a similar status to the zebu in India.)

The zebu are probably of aurochs stock, and were domesticated in Asia by 4,000 B.C. Divided into many breeds, they differ mainly from European cattle in having a much enlarged fatty hump on the shoulder. Usually they possess a big dewlap, short horns, and long ears. Some breeds are much smaller than the typical ox.

Throughout India, people hold the oxen in high esteem and they rarely eat the flesh—except that of an animal that has died. It is not unusual to hear an Indian call a dear friend of his "my ox".

India is not the only home of the humped cattle. They are also found in China, the East Indies, and East Africa. In these areas the animals are kept for meat and milk, for riding, and as beasts of burden. Humped cattle have been introduced in Texas and other places, where they have been crossed with other breeds, producing a variety of animal that can resist Texas fever, an infectious disease of cattle.

FAMOUS "WILD CATTLE" OF BRITAIN

One of the mysteries of science are the famous so-called "wild cattle" of England's Chartley Park and Chillingham Park, and Cadzow Castle in Scotland. Although these oxen closely resemble some of our finest modern breeds, they are fairly wild creatures, having been kept in surroundings much like those that wild cattle enjoy in Nature.

No one is sure where the "wild cattle" originated. Some have said they were half-tame descendants of the aurochs, but this is doubtful. We have records of herds of wild white cattle that roamed England long ago, and they may have been put into enclosures as the woodlands were cut down.

It was reported of the white cattle of Chillingham Park that they had a number of savage traits. The cows kept their young in hiding for seven days or longer after they were born. The bulls were said to engage in combat over a likely female, and once in a while one of the contestants was slain.

As a schoolboy, the author lived near the place where the Chartley wild cattle were kept. They had a very picturesque appearance, with their coats snow white except for the feet, ear tips, and the end of the nose, which were always jet black. At first there were forty of these animals, but their number gradually dwindled until only one big bull and a cow were left.

One Sunday morning the schoolboy crept up behind that last big bull and breathlessly tied some strands of the hair of its tail to the park railing. It was a tense few minutes until the boy reached safety. Later he returned and found some of the bull's hairs still attached to the railing.

That adventure was over forty years ago. The last time the author was in England, he came across that bunch of long white hairs, duly tagged and labelled, in his old desk. It is an interesting memento, for the Chartley herd has become extinct.

YAKS, OR GRUNTING OXEN

The Yak or Grunting Ox, *Bos* (*Poephagus*) *grunniens*, got its second name from the gruntlike sounds it makes, especially when it is loaded beyond comfortable capacity.

In the wild, the yak frequents the plateau of Tibet, among the coldest and most desolate parts of the world, at elevations of fourteen thousand to fifteen thousand feet in winter—up to twenty thousand in summer.

A USEFUL ANIMAL

The domesticated yak, a somewhat smaller animal, has served its country well—it might almost be taken as a symbol of Tibet. This buffalo-like animal is milked (Tibetans have many uses for rancid yak butter, and are fond of it in tea); it is ridden, driven, and carries heavy loads over mountain passes. In this lofty land where there are few motor roads and the people are not governed by pressure of time, the yak can fulfil almost all their transportation needs.

HAIR SO LONG IT SWEEPS THE GROUND

Easy to recognize is the yak or grunting ox, with its long, smooth hair growing down over its entire body, hiding the feet. Tassels of hair even obscure its eyes and ears. Found only in the remote fastnesses of Tibet, the yak, when domesticated, is highly valued for its surefootedness and ability to carry heavy loads up steep inclines.

A MASSIVE BEAST

Large yak bulls are nearly six feet high at the shoulder and weigh twelve hundred pounds. The legs are short, with large, rounded feet, and the muzzle and ears are relatively small. Smooth, round horns curve upwards, outwards, and then forwards. The hair on the back is smooth but very long on the lower parts, hanging from the sides of the body in a long, sweeping fringe. (Yak hair is widely employed by the Tibetans, and a team of yaks may be harnessed by rope made of their own hair.) The yak's general colour is dark brown, almost black, throughout—except for a little white on the muzzle.

The Yak's Tail. The yak's tail has a thick tassel of long hair. At one time this plumed tail was in great demand; it was used in the head-dress worn by officers of state to denote their rank. The tails were also dyed and mounted on a sabre handle, and used as fly swatters. Many of the domestic animals, such as the plough yak (ploughing in Tibet is done with yaks) are now tailless—the tail has been cut off and sold.

SURE-FOOTED AND HARDY MOUNTAINEERS

Yaks feed in the early morning and evening on the rough, wiry grass that grows in the upland valleys. During the day these sure-footed and hardy mountaineers retreat to rest on the steep, barren hillsides, where they command a wide view of the surrounding country. Their sight and hearing are not exceptionally good, but they have a well-developed sense of smell.

During the summer, cows and calves collect in herds of ten to one hundred.

The bulls are more or less solitary, except during the rut; at this time each bull separates four or five cows from the herd. Mating takes place in winter, and the calves are born in the autumn, ten months later.

GAURS—INDIA'S "BISON"

The Gaur, or Seladang, *Bibos gaurus*, is among the largest of wild cattle.

This forest animal, the so-called Indian "bison", attains a height of over six feet at the shoulder, and has a head-and-body length of nine feet, six inches.

Like the yak, the full-grown bull is dark brown, almost black, though the legs from the knees and hocks down are white. The upturned horns are broad, heavy, and tipped with black.

The cows, which are smaller than the bulls, stand about five feet high at the shoulder, and their colouring has rather a reddish cast. The gaur's body is deep through the chest and very massive, with a high ridge from the neck to the middle of the back.

Grasses and shoots of the bamboo and other trees make up the principal diet of the gaur, which keeps to the forest and tall grass, generally near the hills, in India, Burma, and the Malay Peninsula. A shy and timid animal, this sizable creature travels in small herds of five to twenty or more.

Most of the natives and hunters agree that the gaur is a very inoffensive creature, rarely attacking anyone; the bull which has been expelled from the herd may, however, be inclined to make trouble. A wounded animal is also dangerous. Hunting the gaur was a favourite sport of the Englishman in India; if his first shots did not kill the gaur, the hunter sometimes had to face the deadly rush of the agonized beast.

Attempts to raise the gaur as a domestic animal have failed—unless, of course, it could be proved that the gayal (described later) is a breed of gaur. Calves always die in captivity before they grow up.

The natives of Malabar have a rather fanciful legend about the gaur. They assert that it will pick up stones in its nostrils and discharge them at adversaries with the force of a musket ball; that their aim is so accurate that the wound is always mortal.

The Gayal, or Mithan, *Bibos frontalis*, dwells in the same forests as its big cousin the gaur, but depends on man for its food. The animal is very similar in colour and general appearance to the gaur, though somewhat smaller, with shorter limbs and a less pronounced ridge on the back.

The horns are broad and heavy, but are nearly straight instead of curved like those of the gaur. The range of this species of cattle includes the hills of Tipperah and the regions south of the Assam Valley in India.

The gayal is used by the natives for food and for its milk; we have reason to believe that the gayal is actually a half-domesticated race of the gaur.

OTHER INTERESTING WILD OXEN OF THE EAST

The Banting, or Tsaine, *Bibos sondaicus,* the typical wild ox of the Malay lands, resembles a Jersey cow more than anything else. Much smaller, lighter in colour than the gaur, and even more timid, it has been successfully domesticated by the natives.

The common banting lives in Java, but it has close relatives throughout south-eastern Asia. It has much the same habits as the gaur, though it prefers low-lying grassy plains and bamboo forests to the more hilly homeland of the gaur.

The Kouprey, *Bibos sauveli,* is also known as the Grey Ox and Indo-Chinese Forest Ox. Strange as it may seem, it escaped the attention of science until a little over twenty years ago, when a living specimen was sent to the zoological gardens in Paris.

Another interesting thing about the kouprey is that the horns of the adult male burst open at the tip, exposing about five inches of an inner black horn.

A typical oxlike animal, the kouprey is over five feet at the shoulder. Its head-and-body length is eight feet, and the tail is quite long—over three feet. The hair is short, close, glossy, and blackish brown in colour, with occasional white markings down the back. The feet are usually white.

The kouprey, so far as we know, is found only in Cambodia and Laos.

AFRICAN BUFFALOES

CAPE BUFFALOES—SAVAGE WHEN ROUSED

The Black or Cape Buffalo, *Syncerus caffer,* is suspicious but inoffensive when unmolested. Hunted, it becomes wary and usually seeks safety in flight. When persistently stalked, and especially if it is wounded, the animal will hide in the bush, then savagely charge the hunter when he approaches within twenty feet of the ambuscade. At such close range, almost nothing less than a smashing direct hit in the brain will stop the fierce onslaught of the maddened beast.

The Hunter Hunted. One fiction writer on African bush lore tells a most amazing story about the ferocity of the black buffalo. A huntress entering the country of the Masai tribe was attacked by a large bull. When she fired at the charging animal, the bullet grazed the shield of its horns and only creased the top of its head. This infuriated the animal to an even greater degree.

The woman barely had time to dismount her horse, which took the brunt of the charge. Taking refuge up a small thorn tree, she saw the horse gored to death. As she watched in horrified silence, the maddened bull, with deep, guttural roars, trampled and ripped its victim until the veldt was spattered with blood and gore. Then, instead of making off, the bull sniffed the air for the rider. Presently he located the tree in which the woman clung. Vainly he tried to dislodge her by repeated charges at the tree.

The woman, who had long experience in hunting, prepared to spend the night in the tree. It swayed as she strapped herself with her belt to a high branch, but she was safe enough—or so it seemed. Now comes the most incredible part of the story.

The least of the black buffalo's virtues is persistence. Finding he could not shake her or hook her down by plunging upward in the air, the bull discovered there was another way to get at her—that by stretching his neck and head to the fullest extent upward, he could reach the girl's bare legs with his long, rough tongue.

The girl could climb no higher—her knees were already pressed under her chin. Having reached her limit, she fearfully realized the things a buffalo can do with its tongue. With horror she recalled what had happened to others in the same predicament. Native folklore tells of many such tragedies.

Next morning she was found with the flesh gone from both her feet—licked away to above her ankles by the rasplike tongue of the beast. When help came, the gory bull was still standing beneath the tree, the blood dripping from his mouth and nose. The buffalo paid with his life, but that night the girl died through loss of blood.

We might be tempted to write off this story as a product of the author's imagination. However, Afrikanders who have read the story and are familiar with the ferocious nature of the Cape buffalo, concede that such an incident could be true, or that it is within the realm of possibility.

Remarkable Horns. The Cape buffalo is a large, thickset black buffalo with massive horns, a short head, and large, fringed ears. The broadly flattened horns rise close together on the top of the head, where they form a helmet-like shield, then extend backwards and outwards, curving up evenly to a sharp point.

Viewed from above, the horns are somewhat like triangles—very broad at the base (sometimes more than twelve inches) and tapered sharply to the tip. The total length along the outer curve of the horn is up to thirty-nine inches. A full-grown bull stands about five feet high at the shoulder and weighs about fifteen hundred pounds.

Where the Cape Buffalo Lives. The ideal dwelling place for the Cape buffalo contains an ample supply of water, a large pasture of grass and reeds, and a background of forest or jungle for shelter. Under such conditions, herds may range from fifty up to a thousand.

African buffaloes feed during the early morning and late evening and often at night, but they rest in the bush during the heat of the day. Usually the buffalo is a very silent creature and large herds,

HUNTERS, BEWARE THE ANGER OF THIS BUFFALO

Unmolested, the Cape or black buffalo of Africa keeps to itself and harms no one. But when it is hunted down, and particularly if wounded, it fights back with maddened and bloody fury. On this animal's handsome head rests a magnificent pair of horns—each may measure over three feet in length.

[7-1]

The okapi descended side by side with the giraffe from a common ancestor, and is considered the "normal" member of the family. Otherwise built like a giraffe, with its relatively short neck, zebra stripes and donkey ears, the okapi secreted itself in the African forests and remained a "myth" for almost 2,000 years after its skyscraper cousin was universally accepted as a reality.

See page 758

Until Julius Caesar imported one into Rome in 46 B.C., the western world believed the giraffe to be a mythical creature, "camelopard-alis", its father a leopard, its mother a camel. The Arabs who knew it called it "zarafa"—a creature of grace and one who walks swiftly; on firm dry ground the tall heavy-bodied giraffe is indeed a fleet and graceful pacer. *See page 752*

[7-1A]

[7-2]

A small female giraffe will weigh more than half a ton, a large
bull two tons. As they grow older, many giraffes come to the
conclusion that shifting this bulk with the attendant bending and
unbending of legs is more bother than it's worth—they sleep
standing up. A well-placed 12-inch hoof or 100-pound head
brought down with the force of a pile driver, insures a giraffe
the reasonably peaceful existence it prefers. *See page 752*

when feeding, never make a sound. The buffalo will bellow when attacked by lions. However, they prefer to hunt the cows and calves rather than the big-horned bulls that can put up a terrific battle against a single lion.

Cape buffaloes have a normal life span of at least sixteen years; some have lived ten years in captivity. The mating season starts in January, and the calves are born eleven months later.

The African buffalo is spread over most of Africa south of the Sahara, but disease and hunting have greatly reduced its numbers. Like most other big game, this buffalo suffers severely from rinderpest, which is spread by the domestic cattle of wandering natives. On one occasion, a rinderpest epidemic practically reduced to zero the entire buffalo population of Kenya for nearly twenty years.

The Dwarf Forest Buffalo, *Syncerus nanus*, sometimes called the Bush Cow, dwells in the forested regions of central and western Africa. A distinct species, it is much smaller than the Cape buffalo. The shoulder height is about four feet, the dressed weight about 580 pounds. The coat is typically red, but bulls turn black with advancing age. The horns, flattened at the base, are directed in a backward curve and do not exceed thirty inches in length.

BISON—ONCE THERE WERE MILLIONS

The American Bison, or Plains Buffalo, *Bison bison*, once roamed the North American plains in vast herds of as many as four million individuals. One single herd would cover an area twenty-five miles wide and fifty miles deep. The total number of bisons in North America at the time the white man arrived has been estimated at sixty million. By 1900, only three hundred of these huge creatures were left in the United States. Today there are several times this number in Yellowstone National Park, where they are prospering.

Civilized man has never beheld a greater concentration of big game than the buffalo herds in their heyday. Not only the Indians, but the early western settlers as well, depended largely on the buffalo for their livelihood. The great beast furnished the materials for food, clothing, shelter, and heat.

In the end, the very profusion of bison led to their downfall, as we shall see later on.

EAL / 7—C

CLIFF STAMPEDES

The Indians used to make a practice of stampeding herds of bison over a cliff. Perhaps the most famous of these natural death traps for the bison was Buffalo Jump-off in the valley of the Yellowstone, Montana.

In its day this well-known cliff was a primitive form of the slaughter-yards of Chicago, as the Indians periodically drove the herds over the brink.

The Indians made robes of the buffalo's hide. They cut the meat into thin strips, which they smoked and dried; it was known as "jerked meat" or "jerky" and was almost as hard as a rock. They carried it on journeys, and, when they wanted to eat it, pounded the strips into powder and mixed them with berries and fat. This fare went under the name of pemmican. By way of contrast, today's pemmican, used by explorers, is likely to contain dried beef, suet, raisins, and sugar.

BUFFALO PATHFINDERS

Many of America's historic highways were originally buffalo trails. The beasts knew and followed the best routes through mountain passes and across the continent.

Great steel and concrete highways now proceed along the trails once trodden by bison.

BISON COUNTRY

The typical bison is primarily a plains animal—it favours open, flat grass country bare of trees yet well supplied with water. The centre of abundance of the American bison was the great plains of the Mississippi River valley, where the land was unforested and well watered. Here, and here only, was the bison found in herds of millions.

Formerly the bison roamed over most of the United States with the exception of the arid deserts and the Pacific coast region. In the West, the range extended north to Great Slave Lake in Canada; southward these beasts reached into north-eastern Mexico. Continually on the move, the herds ran no danger of overgrazing, despite their excessive numbers.

PORTRAIT OF A BEHEMOTH

A great, powerful beast with a massive head and neck and humped shoulders, the bison is, however, surprisingly narrow, especially in the hind quarters. A thick mantle of long, shaggy hair envelops the head, neck, and forelimbs but stops abruptly at the shoulders. A long black beard hangs from the chin of adult males, and the rest of the body is covered with comparatively short, close hair. The short, stout horns curve out and upward, while the tail, though short, carries a tassel of long hair.

Average full-grown bulls measure over five feet high at the shoulder and weigh around sixteen hundred pounds. The record weight is three thousand pounds. Cows are considerably smaller, weighing from seven hundred to nine hundred pounds. The general colour of the animal's coat is a rich dark brown, becoming almost black on the head and shoulders.

With the coming of spring and the moulting season, the black cape fades to a pale yellowish brown.

THE RUTTING SEASON

At the approach of the rutting season in June and July, the bulls fight for supremacy of the herd. Battles between two evenly matched bulls may last two days and a night in succession. The animals often struggle until both are exhausted, and sink to their knees; then they take up the fight again after a brief rest. When the issue has been settled, the victor is comparatively quiet, presumably too busy with his females to remember his recent quarrelsome feelings; as for the vanquished bull, he bellows incessantly, day and night. Bulls rarely make an unprovoked attack on man, even during the rutting season.

The calves may come any time between April and June, but most of them are born in May, nine and one-half months after the adults have mated.

Usually there is only one calf; occasionally there are twins. The newborn calf's coat is bright tawny, almost yellow, with a dark reddish band down the middle of the back. By the time the mother has licked her offspring from head to foot, the calf is ready to stand on its shaky legs for its first meal.

Most animals will turn their back to a storm—not so the bison.

Better clothed in front than behind, it will meet a blizzard of driving snow and bitter cold with its head directed into the wind.

BISON OF MOUNTAIN AND WOODS

Among the bison that are now extinct in the United States, one mountain-dwelling form lived in Colorado, while another type frequented the forests and hills of Maryland, Pennsylvania, and Virginia.

THE BISON, STALWART WILD OX OF FRONTIER AMERICA

The bison or plains buffalo once roamed the United States and Canada in hordes four million strong; their flesh and hides provided the necessities of life for the pioneers. Bison trails were so good that the highways of today were built upon them. This strong and dignified animal, with its massive face and black beard, now remains largely as a symbol of a courageous chapter in America's past.

The Wood Bison, a third variety, is larger and taller than the plains bison. The last of the truly wild bison, it still exists in the remote Slave River region of northern Alberta in Canada. The shoulder height of grown bulls may exceed six feet. These animals are marked by a broad brown band extending down the middle of the back.

VIGIL IN THE SNOW

That the behaviour of wild animals is often unpredictable is well illustrated by this striking experience which the author had when he was in the Slave River district of northern Alberta, collecting a group of wood bison for the Canadian National Museum. The expedition's efforts were crowned with success—the writer shot two bison. Then, for a while, he was all alone in the wilderness; his companions went off to make contact with the hunting party's aircraft. One of the men had borrowed the author's rifle, leaving him without any weapon but his knife, which he needed in order to skin his bison.

Soon it began to snow. The author paused to rest from the tiresome job of skinning. Glancing around, he saw a big bull bison standing motionless not fifty yards away, and staring straight at him. Next time the writer looked up, the bison was still there, snow drifting in its face.

From another direction there appeared two bears, then came a third, standing up on their hind legs and watching intently . . . if not hungrily.

By dark, one skin was off. The author thought of pulling it over himself to keep warm, but it was not improbable that the animal spectators might take him for a dead buffalo, and an excellent candidate for their next meal; it seemed better to stay cold and keep the respect they owed him as a human being. He heard a piercing wolf call that sent cold shivers down his back. Then another and another wolf answered. Finally all was silent in the pitch-black night and he fell asleep. About midnight, the writer woke up, fancying that he could hear some creature breathing not more than ten paces away. A wolf was outlined against the snow. Soon it vanished into the night. Next morning, when the sun rose, all the visitors were gone.

CORTES AND THE BISON

Most books tell us that the Spanish explorer Hernando Cortés was the first European to view the bison. In 1519, so goes the story, Cortés stood in the courtyard of Montezuma's palace after having fought his way to the Aztec capital, now Mexico City. There he saw a strange creature with a humped back and shaggy coat which he described as a "rare composite of several divers animals".

The source of this story is Solis' *Historia de la Conquista de Mejico*. However, it seems that Solis never was in Mexico. He may have assumed that Cortés had seen one in the Aztec emperor's zoo, and proceeded to invent an account of such a visit.

On the other hand, Bernal Díaz del Castillo, who was a member of the Cortés expedition, described Montezuma's zoo in detail. His book mentions tigers, lions (not the African varieties, of course), and foxes, as well as a rattlesnake and a great variety of colourful birds; but he makes no reference to anything like a bison. Cortés's fame will thus have to rest on his conquests exclusively—the bison will henceforth have no part in it.

WHO WAS "BUFFALO BILL"?

That famous buffalo hunter, frontiersman, and scout, William F. Cody, has gone down in American history as "Buffalo Bill". He was, however, not the only one to bear that title. There were many "Buffalo Bills", each claiming sole right to that name.

William Mathewson was perhaps the first to be named "Buffalo" and acquired the title during the great drought of 1860. A quiet, unassuming fellow, he earned the gratitude of the starving people of western Kansas by feeding them with large quantities of buffalo meat.

Cody was of course the traditional Buffalo Bill, with his inseparable buffalo horse Brigham and his equally inseparable buffalo gun, by name "Lucretia Borgia". Cody acquired his title in 1867 when the Kansas Pacific Railway pushed into buffalo country. The railroad company hired Cody to kill buffalo because the beasts were a nuisance in the vicinity of a railway route and because they attracted Indians, who were becoming very troublesome at that time. By slaughtering buffalo, the white man deprived the Plains Indians of their chief source of food.

It was the railroad hands that gave William F. Cody the title of "Buffalo Bill."

Colonel Charles J. Jones, better known as "Buffalo" Jones, was famous for his lassoing ability (earlier we saw how he used it in Africa), and was largely responsible for collecting the buffalo herd in Yellowstone National Park today. He was appointed park warden in 1902. Jones trained a pair of bison to haul a cart and later used them to plough the land.

WISENTS—EUROPE'S BIGGEST MAMMALS

The Wisent, or European Bison, *Bison bonasus*, once at home in many of the forests of Asia and Europe, including England, is now extinct in the wild state; the few remaining animals are in the Duke of Bedford's park at Woburn, England.

A typical bison in appearance, the wisent has humped shoulders covered with a close curly mane. The rest of the body is covered with short, thick, woolly brown hair. The horns are short, rounded, and curled slightly upward.

EUROPE'S NEARLY EXTINCT BISON

The wisent or European bison, like its American kin, has powerful mane-covered shoulders rising to a hump, a large neck and head, and hindparts that look slender by comparison with the rest of its body. Two World Wars have wiped out this animal from those parts of eastern Europe where it once lived.

Larger than its American cousin, the European bison (or aurochs, as it is often erroneously known) has a mane which is shorter and less shaggy than the New World bison's. The bull of the European bison is the largest of the native European mammals. Weighing up to two thousand pounds, it stands over six feet at the shoulder, and measures over ten feet from the nose to the root of the tail.

Under the protection of the Russian tsars, the wisent existed in fair numbers in the forests of Bielowitza, Lithuania, and the Kuban

ANTELOPES—RENOWNED FOR GRACE AND SPEED

district in the Caucasus until the beginning of the First World War. However, such wisents as remained in these places were exterminated in the Second World War.

Antelopes—Renowned for Grace and Speed

THE ANTELOPES are famous for their speed, grace, and good looks. Generally creatures of light and slender build, they are nevertheless of many shapes and sizes. In this big group of animals we find, for example, the Royal Antelope, which stands only ten inches at the shoulder—and, by way of startling contrast, the Giant Eland, an oxlike animal that weighs twelve hundred pounds.

Among antelopes' horns there is a great deal of difference, too. As a rule, an antelope's horns rise from the head and then sweep backwards. Yet some horns are straight, some spiral shaped, others lyre shaped; still others have fantastic curves. There are even antelopes with four horns instead of two. Among some kinds of antelope, both sexes have horns; among others, only the males are horned. Even the length of the horns shows startling variations—on the smaller antelopes we find horns that are mere stubs, while the larger animals may have horns forty inches long.

Some antelopes gather in herds of anywhere up to ten thousand, others are shy, elusive, solitary creatures. Where do these cud-chewers live? In all sorts of places—marshes and swamps, deserts, open plains, dense forest, and mountains. Africa is the home of most antelopes; there are also some that are native to Asia. We do not find these animals outside the Old World. Their closest relative in America is the mountain goat.

One thing in general may be safely said about the antelopes: they are the most graceful and most decorative of all the members of the family Bovidae.

THE ANTELOPE IN ANCIENT TIMES

The hartebeest was one of the few African antelopes known to ancient writers. Herodotus includes it among the beasts of Libya. Aristotle, Aeschylus, and Pliny also mentioned the hartebeest.

The name "antelope" seems to be of fabulous origin. According to one authority, it was originally derived from a Coptic word signifying "unicorn".

Naturalists in ancient times used the term "antelope" to designate an imaginary animal that lived on the banks of the Euphrates and cut down trees by using its horns as a saw. In fact, Linnaeus, many centuries later, placed the antelope among the fabulous animals, in the first edition of his great work on natural history. In a later edition he ignored the antelope altogether.

Few people realize that, strictly speaking, the blackbuck of India is the only true antelope in the world. The word "antelope", as a scientific name, is applied only to the blackbuck. As far as the early writers were concerned, it was *the antelope*—there were no others.

ANTELOPES WITH SPIRAL HORNS

GREATER KUDUS—FINEST OF THEIR TRIBE

The "Antelope King". The Greater Kudu, *Strepsiceros strepsiceros*, a large creature with lengthy corkscrew horns, is one of the stateliest-looking antelopes in all Africa. Sometimes called "the antelope king", it has been described as the finest of all its tribe—and not without reason.

Shy and Elusive, Yet Courageous. In their dances of triumph to celebrate the killing of a lion, the natives often give periodic blasts from their traditional kudu horn trumpets. This is about as near to a wild greater kudu as the average hunter or traveller will ever get. Outside parks and game reserves, the kudu is extremely timid and elusive.

If one is to see the greater kudu at all, it will be in the bush or in scrub-covered rocky hills, where the animal can climb like a goat and keep a sharp watch for approaching danger. It is helped by the camouflage of its striped grey coat, which is difficult to make out in the bush.

When the kudu is hunted, and hard pressed by dogs, it will take to the rivers, swimming steadily downstream. Usually it outdistances its pursuers in the water. At times, it proves to be a most courageous animal—when cornered or wounded, it will attempt to defend itself against both man and dogs. Hunters say that an experienced old bull, once it knows it is being tracked, will try to startle a less mature kudu out of the bush, so that the attention of the pursuers will be diverted. How true this is, only the old bull can definitely answer.

IT APPEARS TO BE FOR EVER IN FLIGHT

This African antelope, rarely glimpsed by man, is known as the greater kudu. An adept climber, it lives among rocky hills, where it can maintain a lookout for danger. The male has horns like giant corkscrews, but the cow is hornless. During the rutting season, when males fight for a mate, their horns sometimes become fatally interlocked.

Corkscrew Horns. The glory of the kudu bull is its magnificent horns. They may reach a length of sixty inches or more, and are fashioned in the form of long, wide, open spirals of two and one-half turns; cows are hornless.

This proud, erect animal stands almost five feet at the shoulder, and bulls weigh between five hundred and seven hundred pounds. The coat is greyish brown in colour with vertical white stripes along the sides of the body. The face is bedecked with white markings on the nose, cheeks, and around the eyes. The kudu's ears are large, the tail moderately long and tufted; there is a fringe of long hair on the throat of both male and female.

The Rutting Season. Except during the breeding season, when small herds or family groups are the rule, the sexes live apart, and the males keep bachelor quarters. Bulls fight during the rut, and occasionally this results in inseparably locked antlers.

The deep, hoarse barks or "bugles" of the kudus are the loudest sounds made by any antelope.

Cows usually have one calf at a time, seven or eight months after mating. Kudus have survived in captivity for over eleven years.

The range of the greater kudu and its local relatives extends from Ethiopia to South Africa.

In the bush and rocky hill country which it loves, its favourite food consists of leaves, grasses, and wild fruits.

LESSER KUDUS—REMARKABLE JUMPERS

The Lesser Kudu, *Strepsiceros imberbis*, is a remarkable jumper. It can cover over thirty feet in a single leap over bushes; it almost seems to be flying as it hurtles gracefully through the air, six feet above the ground.

Similar to the greater kudu in appearance, this lesser relative is much smaller; the colours are brighter, the horns less divergent, there is no fringe on the throat. Vertical stripes adorn the lesser kudu's body, while a white arrow bridges the nose below the eyes. The shoulder height is usually under forty inches.

A very timid and inoffensive creature, the lesser kudu is found in the dry, bush-covered plains from Somaliland to Kenya in north-eastern Africa.

SITATUNGAS—BUCKS OF THE MARSHES

The Sitatunga, or Marsh Buck, *Limnotragus spekii*, comes as close to being a water animal as any antelope. Its home is the big swamps and watercourses of central and eastern Africa. In the sitatunga's damp haunts, the natives usually pursue the wary beast in dugout canoes; in the dry season they are able to fire the bush and drive the sitatunga out into the open.

The Sitatunga in the Water. The sitatunga can swim, dive, and travel a considerable distance under water. When frightened, it frequently takes refuge in deep water, often lying submerged with only the nostrils and eyes above the surface. Its feet are especially adapted for a life near water. The halves of the long, slender hoofs spread widely when the animal walks or runs, thus providing ample support on a tangled mass of weeds. On the soft mud it leaves a V-shaped spoor.

The sitatunga never ventures out into the open to feed except at night; when disturbed, it makes for the nearest marsh or swamp. On hard ground it is clumsy, even awkward, and can be overtaken by a fast runner.

Grown male sitatungas stand a bit less than four feet at the shoulder. Their hair is brown, with stripes. Males have spiral horns twenty-eight inches long measured in a straight line from base to tip, and thirty-five inches following the spiral curve. Females are hornless. They and the young are of a bright chestnut colour, with white stripings and spottings, as a rule.

BUSHBUCKS—DANGEROUS WHEN WOUNDED

The Bushbuck, or Harnessed Antelope, *Tragelaphus scriptus*, is a lover of solitude; it lives alone, or at most in pairs during the breeding season. Active only by night, it lies up by day in dense brush. Both sexes utter a hoarse bark, but the male has a louder and harsher note than the female.

Timid in the Wild, Aggressive in Captivity. The bushbuck is one of the wariest of African antelopes and frequently takes to water. It generally trusts for safety to its wariness and the concealment offered by the bush. The bushbuck is rather noisy, however, and utters its deep bark when it hears unusual sounds or smells a man or a leopard. When wounded, the animal often proves to be quite dangerous. There are instances of rams killing a man, a leopard, and a wild dog. In captivity the bushbuck is very aggressive; the rams may kill or severely injure the ewes.

The males of the subspecies of bushbuck differ greatly in colour, varying from a nearly black animal to a bright chestnut. All forms have white stripes running down each side, two slantwise stripes, a dozen or so white spots on the hind limbs, and a white band across the chest. The young and the females are always a bright chestnut with characteristic white stripings. A small antelope, the bushbuck seldom stands more than three feet at the shoulder; its simple spiral horns rarely exceed eighteen inches in length. There is a fringe of stiff, erect hairs along the back.

A STUDY IN SOLITUDE

Deep in the forests of southern Africa, the bushbuck or harnessed antelope leads a shy and hermit-like existence. Only at mating time is this lonely creature seen in pairs. On its beautiful russet-coloured coat are vivid stripes and spots of pure white.

The bushbuck is found in many parts of Africa south of the Sahara, and there are well over twenty named geographical forms. Primarily a forest animal, it also occurs in the thorn-bush country and may feed in the open-range country bordering the forestlands. Occasionally it invades and damages gardens and farmlands.

Bushbucks breed at all seasons of the year and the young are born from six to seven and one-half months after mating time.

THE NYALA—HANDSOME ANTELOPE OF ZULULAND

The Nyala, *Tragelaphus angasii*, is a handsome, short-haired antelope with a distinct colour pattern for each sex. "Nyala" or "Myala" is the native Zulu name for this most beautiful antelope.

A relative of the bushbuck, the nyala frequents the hot, low country and more or less open bush near rivers and lakes in Zululand and the neighbouring country.

Occasionally the nyala is solitary, but more often it is seen in small parties of females and young, or equal numbers of males and females. Often the males spar together with their horns; but once the rutting season arrives, they battle in real earnest.

BEAUTIFUL MARKINGS

Males are slate grey and stand about forty-two inches at the shoulder. They have spiral horns that measure twenty-four inches in a straight line and thirty inches with the curves. The females are hornless and reddish chestnut in colour. Both sexes are beautifully marked with numerous vertical white stripes on the body and a white spinal fringe extending from the shoulders to the base of the tail.

How the Nyala Is Trapped. The occasions on which you can get a fleeting glimpse of this handsome beast are apt to be few and far between. When surprised, it is off like a flash, leaping over the bushes, its horns laid back and nose outstretched, to disappear in the dark recesses of the bush.

Natives trap the nyala by enclosing its much-frequented haunts and leaving little gaps in the fence. In each trap there is a noose of stout cord made of tough fibre. One end of the cord is fastened to a sapling which is bent over the gap and held in place by a trigger. As the nyala steps through the gap, it releases the spring sapling, one of the animal's legs, caught in the noose, is hoisted in the air and so the nyala can neither struggle nor try to escape.

The Mountain Nyala, largest of the bushbuck types, occurs in the highlands of southern Ethiopia. It stands four and one-half feet at the shoulder.

ELANDS—BIGGEST OF ANTELOPES

Strictly an African animal, the Eland, *Taurotragus*, got its name from the Dutch settlers. *Eland* is the Dutch word for "elk", an appropriate name, the Dutch felt, for the largest species of antelope they had encountered. Actually the eland is quite different from either the elk or other antelopes. A heavy fold of skin—a dewlap—hangs from the bull's neck, and this enormous creature is rather oxlike in appearance.

A Great Traveller. For all its large size, the eland is swift and agile. It will often spring into the air, leaping high over the back of one of its fellows.

THE ANTELOPE HEAVYWEIGHT

An outsized antelope, the giant eland tips the scales at twelve hundred pounds. Despite its bulk, the eland has the speed, grace, and agility typical of antelopes. It can leap high into the air—even over the back of another eland—with acrobatic ease. Distinctive of the eland is a loose flap of skin hanging from its neck.

The eland is continually on the move. Alarmed, it makes off at an exceedingly fast trot which produces a faint clicking sound. This sound, attributed to the click of the hoofs, can be heard for quite a distance.

A horse has to extend itself to full gallop to keep up with a herd of elands.

When disturbed or suspicious of danger, an eland always runs against the wind. It can be swerved to one side or the other, but it will not run downwind. An eland will charge a man on horseback who happens to be directly in its way, rather than face about. However, this is the only time that the eland will make an aggressive move against man.

Where the Eland Lives. The eland favours country in between the open veldt and forest country. Though it feeds far out on the open plains, it prefers to rest in the shelter of trees during the midday heat. Loving society at all times, the eland assembles periodically in migratory treks.

On such occasions, several groups may be seen together, associated in oversized herds.

This beast can live independent of water, but where water is available it will drink twice a day during the dry season. It grazes where it can get fresh young grass; it also browses on leaves and twigs of trees.

Of all antelopes, the eland is the closest to the cattle. It is surprising that this animal has not been domesticated; it is easily tamed, not aggressive, of large size, and its meat is of fine quality.

The Common Eland, *Taurotragus oryx*, ranges from Kenya Colony to South Africa and Angola, where it frequents grassy plains in herds of about fifty and sometimes as many as two hundred. It is often found in company with other antelope and zebra.

The bull of the common eland stands from five and one-half to six feet in shoulder height and may weigh up to twelve hundred pounds. The animal's coat is a pale fawn with a few white body stripes, but old bulls are rather near blue grey in colour. It is curious that the spirally twisted horns are longer in cows than in bulls—thirty-three inches following the twist.

The common eland's breeding season begins at the end of March and extends into May. The young are born about 256 days after mating

The yak, wild or domestic, inhabits the cold, desolate plateau of Tibet. Domesticated, the huge, sure-footed, patient animal is milked, plucked, ridden and driven by Tibetans—often harnessed to a heavy load by a rope made of its own hair. In spite of their large size, wild yaks frequent the higher altitudes, ranging up to 20,000 feet in summer.

See page 773

Largest of the oxen, the Asiatic or water buffalo has a 5,000-year record of faithful domestic service, but it also still exists in the wild state. From appearances only it is difficult to distinguish the two—the unreasonably savage disposition of the wild animal is a reliable test, but not to be undertaken lightly. *See page 768*

[7-4]

When pioneers joined forces with Indians in its wholesale slaughter the American bison almost disappeared. By 1900 only 300 of the sombre-faced plains buffaloes remained but today, with the protection of stringent conservation measures, their number is increasing. Its massive head, neck and shoulders enveloped in a thick mantle of long shaggy hair and its slender hind quarters scantily covered, the bison is one animal which never turns its back on a blizzard. *See page 779*

[7-5]

Unmolested, the Cape buffalo of Africa is suspicious but inoffensive; hunted, it becomes wary; persistently stalked or wounded, it becomes a wildly violent, doggedly determined killer. Spread over most of Africa south of the Sahara, the big black buffalo, like the bison, has suffered severely from hunters and disease. · *See page 776*

[7-5A]

Surprised or startled, the handsome Nyala antelope of Zululand is off like a flash, but on rare occasions it will stand long enough to be admired. The unsuspecting female in the background has her own distinct colour pattern, but both have the white spinal ridge and vertical side markings.
See page 792

The pronghorn combines certain traits of deer and antelope but its overall characteristics are so at variance with both that scientists have placed it in a family all by itself. Possibly the only living hoofed mammal native to America, and by far the swiftest runner on the continent, its curiosity has all but proved its undoing.

See page 761

[7-6]

[7-6A]

In a land of elusive animals, the bongo or broad horned antelope of the bamboo forests of West Africa so rarely shows itself that it is one of the most coveted trophies of big game hunters. Travelling in small family groups (both sexes have massive horns) the bongos bolt, unseen, at the snap of a twig—and no human can move in the brittle bamboo without announcing his presence. See page 795

takes place. These animals are fairly scarce today in the southern part of their range, having been heavily hunted for their excellent flesh and strong hides.

The Giant Eland, or Derby's Eland, *Taurotragus derbianus*, the largest living antelope, will survive for a long time if the protection afforded it in the Sudan continues to be enforced. More reddish than the common eland, this sturdy creature has a great many white vertical stripes on the sides of the body; the horns are long and massive, particularly in the bulls.

This antelope frequents wooded localities from Senegambia to the Sudan and Portuguese Guinea in West Africa.

BONGOS—PRIZE GAME FOR THE HUNTER

The Bongo, or Broad-horned Antelope, *Boocercus eurycerus*, is one of Africa's most elusive animals. Keeping close to the jungle, it never shows itself in the open. No wonder the bongo is considered one of the most coveted trophies of big-game hunters.

A hunter may spend days winding his way through a trackless bamboo forest in search of this beast and yet be rewarded by nothing more tangible than the hearing of a loud crash in the dense thickets, betokening that a bongo has been startled and has bolted, unseen. To preserve itself, the bongo depends more on its ears than on its eyes or sense of smell. The antelope is fortunate in that no human being can hope to penetrate the jungle of its home grounds without snapping a twig or giving the animal some other indication of his presence. Still, hunters continue to seek it in its native haunts, the dense bamboo forests of West Africa and some of the forested mountain regions of East Africa.

A CHOICE TROPHY

The adult bongo averages a shoulder height of four feet. It has a rich chestnut-red colour with vertical white lines on the sides of the body. Bulls grow darker with age and become black about the head and neck. Both sexes have massive horns that spiral in one complete twist, but the female's are not so large as the male's. The horns are a choice trophy for any hunter.

Old bulls are usually solitary, but the cow and calves and possibly a bull associate in small parties.

EAL / 7—D

THE UNAPPROACHABLE ONE

The bongo will seldom appear in the open; its home is hidden deep in the thick bamboo forests of West Africa. Here, surrounded by a protective screen of trees and dense vegetation, the bongo listens for the faintest sounds of the hunter's movements. Almost invariably, its sensitive ears hear the pursuer in time for the animal to disappear completely into a thicket before it can be shot.

NILGAIS—BLUE BULLS OF INDIA

The Nilgai, or Blue Bull, *Boselaphus tragocamelus*, is common in central India, where it is regarded with reverence because of its colour. The largest Asiatic antelope, it stands about four and one-half feet at the shoulder. In a general way its form is somewhat horselike, but the neck is deep and compressed, while the tail reaches the hocks. The horns are curved spikes—they are rather short (eight to nine inches) and triangular at the base. It is easy to tell the sexes apart. The bull is iron or blue grey in colour, with a tufted throat, while the cow is hornless and fawn coloured. Both sexes have a mane of stiff hairs.

In some localities the nilgai becomes quite tame. It wanders across cultivated lands and is troublesome to crops. However, as the Hindus regard it as a sacred cow, most do not molest it. Sportsmen rarely care to shoot the nilgai; its meat is inferior to that of most Indian wild game.

When alarmed, the nilgai travels at a fast gallop. A bull can only be overtaken by a good horse, while a cow, it is said, cannot be run down by a single rider.

The nilgai can be tamed, but males are often savage in captivity. Some of these animals have been harnessed and taught to draw light carriages; one even allowed itself to be used to carry light loads and human riders.

The nilgai's name, of Persian origin, means "blue ox". We find the big Indian antelope on level or undulating ground, usually where thin brush and scattered trees alternate with open, grassy plains. It is rarely encountered in the thick forest, though it browses on shrubs and low trees in addition to grazing on low herbage.

Each year the cow nilgai gives birth to one young—sometimes a pair —eight to nine months after mating.

Old bulls are often solitary, but parties of fifteen or twenty animals are not unusual.

ANTELOPES WITH FOUR HORNS

The Four-horned Antelope, *Tetracerus quadricornis*, differs as much from other Indian antelopes in habits as in appearance. It is extremely shy and solitary; more than two individuals are rarely seen together.

This antelope dwells along the base of the Himalayas from Punjab to Nepal and in other parts of the Indian Peninsula. Here it frequents scattered forest country and thin bush, and undulating or hilly ground in particular. It moves with a peculiar jerky motion.

Whereas the doe is hornless, the buck, unlike other antelopes, has two pairs of horns; the additional pair, located on the forehead, rarely exceed two inches in length and often exist only as short knobs. The normal or posterior horns are simple spikes not more than four or five inches long.

This antelope's colour is pale brown; an average buck stands two feet at the shoulder and weighs forty-three pounds.

The young—one or two in a litter—are born in January or February, about six months after mating time.

DUIKERS—THEY "DIVE" INTO THE BUSH

Duikers, or duikerboks, are small African antelopes that frequent forest and bush country. They average about two feet in shoulder height.

Duiker means "diver", a name given these small antelopes because of the way they plunge into the underbrush and thickets.

There are at least twenty kinds of duikers; these have been divided into about eighty named geographical forms. In almost all, both sexes have short spiked horns. In general we place these creatures in three groups: bush duikers, blue duikers, and forest duikers. The first group is the commonest.

The Duikerbok, Common Duiker, or Bush Duiker, *Sylvicapra grimmia*, is plentiful over all of Africa, from the Cape of Good Hope to Ethiopia. The colour of the coat varies from greyish brown to bright yellow. The males have short horns; the females are usually, though not always, hornless, unlike other duikers.

——Duikers in the Wild. The duikerbok lives in thick bush country, where it remains concealed until forced to leave; then it gallops off, more like a rabbit than an antelope. Particularly noticeable at such times is the white "flash" of its tail as it dodges from one bush to another or to the nearest patch of cover.

A male and a female usually associate together. When one darts off, its mate is usually concealed at no great distance. However, the two animals usually take off in different directions.

Steinhart, one of the foremost authorities on African game, connects the guinea fowl with the bush duiker and records seeing them at play together. He believes that the sharp-sighted guinea fowl may act as a sentinel. When wounded, caught by one of the big cats or a dog, a duiker will utter a wild scream like a hare. At all other times it is quiet. A young lamb will bleat incessantly when separated from its mother.

Duikers are easily tamed, and will breed in captivity. Some have lived eight or nine years in zoos.

While both sexes are alike in colour, the female may be bigger than the male. The average shoulder height is about twenty inches, while thirty pounds is the maximum weight. The young differ from their parents only in shade of coloration. Several all-white duikers have been recorded.

Though twins are not frequent, they seem to occur more often than among some other African antelopes. The adults mate in October, and about seven months later, generally in May, one or two young are born.

The Zebra Duiker. The Zebra duiker is one of the most strikingly coloured of the many species that are included in this group of small antelopes. A beautiful little creature, it has an orange-red coat marked with tiger-like stripes of black on the back. Inhabiting the dense forest of Sierra Leone, the zebra duiker is known there as the "mountain deer".

WATERBUCKS—AT HOME IN THE WATER

The waterbuck goes about in herds of from five or six to about twenty individuals—though in some groups there may be as many as a hundred. One bull usually has a harem of ten or twelve cows.

A grass feeder, the waterbuck usually occurs on grass flats near water or swampy plains. Where there is waterbuck, you may be sure that water is no more than five or six miles away.

Though it lives on solid ground, the waterbuck, when hunted, will take readily to the water; it is a good swimmer. Followed by dogs, it will turn on them if it possibly can in deep water when it has the advantage. Still, the waterbuck is not a water antelope in the strict sense that the sitatunga is.

The author found waterbuck the least wary of African big game and among the most common. Hunters rarely shoot this animal, probably because its flesh is stringy, coarse, and unpalatable—at least to the white man.

The Defassa, or Sing-sing Waterbuck, *Kobus defassa*, is a large antelope about fifty inches at the shoulder, with coarse, rather long shaggy hair. Males have lengthy, heavily ringed horns, lightly curving backward, upward, and slightly forward at the tip; females are hornless. The defassa waterbuck dwells in western and north-central Africa. Greyish brown in colour, it has a large white patch below the tail.

The Common Waterbuck, *Kobus ellipsiprymnus*, is about the size of the defassa. Large bulls range between four hundred and 550 pounds, bearing horns that measure anywhere up to thirty-nine inches, though the average is considerably less. Darker in colour than the defassa, the common waterbuck is distinguished by a conspicuous white line encircling the rump.

Male waterbucks fight fierce battles for possession of the females. The calves, usually twins, are born eight months after the adults mate. Reddish at first, the young soon change to the mixed grey and black of the grown-ups.

The waterbuck has a wide range extending from South Africa to East Africa and Somaliland. Often it is seen together with wildebeests and zebras.

KOBS, LECHWES, AND REEDBUCKS
WATER-LOVING ANTELOPES

KOBS LIKE COMPANY

Sociable creatures, the kobs usually travel in small parties of seven or eight individuals. Every now and then the small groups join together to form a large herd of fifty animals or more, with both sexes represented.

In its habits the kob is somewhere in between the bushbuck and the lechwe.

It is always found very close to water, and it favours solid ground on which to graze. We never find the kob on the treeless, flooded grass plains where the lechwe is at home.

Buffon's Kob, or the Western Kob, *Adenota kob*, has somewhat lyre-shaped, heavily ringed horns. The general coat colour ranges from rich tawny in the typical form to the brownish black of the white-eared kob of the upper Nile. The young, as well as the females, are reddish brown.

The full-grown adult male measures about thirty-five inches at the shoulder. Kobs are concentrated in Equatorial Africa, from Guinea to Uganda and the swamplands of the Nile.

The Puku, *Adenota vardonii*, is similar to the kob, but has much shorter and heavier horns. It is a reddish-yellow animal, with rather long, wavy hair. The shoulder height is about forty inches, the average weight 190 pounds. The puku frequents the swamps and plains of northern Rhodesia, Nyasaland, and the Zambesi River valley.

LECHWES—PREYED UPON BY CROCODILES

The Lechwe is much more at home in the water than the bushbuck or the kob. Nearly always found in shallow water, the lechwe spends most of its time feeding knee-deep in a swamp. When resting, it lies up at the edge of the water—or even in shallow water.

A strong swimmer, the lechwe, when hard pressed, will make for thick reed beds, where it is hard to find. Crocodiles occasionally get a lechwe.

On one occasion, some natives produced the hide of a lechwe that had been hauled out of the jaws of a crocodile. The natives kill large numbers of lechwes for the flesh, which is quite tasty—far superior to the waterbuck's. The natives hunt the lechwes in canoes; they drive the animals into deep water, where they spear them.

Although it is the most water-loving of all African antelope with the exception of the sitatunga, the lechwe also travels on land in herds of from ten to fifty or more. Disturbed, this antelope moves with a lumbering gait. When the lechwe gallops, its head is lowered and outstretched, with the horns lying back on the shoulders. It is alert and wary; keeping well out in the open when feeding, it will dash for cover to hide at the slightest hint of danger. One of the noisiest of the antelope, the lechwe, once it is alerted, utters a continuous series of croaking grunts.

The Red Lechwe, *Onotragus leche*, has rather long horns. They exceed twice the length of the head and show a slight double curvature. The red lechwe stands about forty inches at the shoulder, and has long, coarse, black hair.

It is common on the plains and in the swamps of northern Rhodesia, Zambesi, and Nyasaland.

The Nile lechwe is a handsome variety which we find in the swamps along the White Nile. The long, slender, double-curved horns are ridged nearly to the tip, and the average shoulder height is about thirty-eight inches. Old bucks are dark brown—almost black—in colour, with a white patch on the shoulders. Females and young are chestnut.

REEDBUCKS—OUT OF THE WATER FOR SAFETY

Strictly creatures of dense cover, the reedbucks rarely show themselves in the open. Nor are they sociable; we are likely to see only one animal alone, or two together—a doe and her fawn, rarely a male and female. These gentle creatures are seldom found more than three or four miles from water. Feeding largely at night or early morning, they haunt tall grass swamps or reed beds.

ANTELOPE OF THE WATERSIDES

The reedbuck is found near many of the lakes and rivers of Africa. There are nine different varieties of this water-loving animal, each varying slightly in its size and the place we find it. Some of these animals prefer high, grassy hillsides, while others favour low swamp-lands. The bohor reedbuck, above, is typically yellowish-red in colour, with a short bushy tail that bobs like a rabbit's when the antelope runs.

One interesting point of difference between the reedbuck and many other antelopes is this: while the reedbuck is always found in the neighbourhood of water, it does not take refuge in it when pursued. Instead, it flees into the dry bush.

Alarmed, the reedbuck moves off with a rocking gait, kicking its heels in the air and flashing its tail, white on the under-side, like a rabbit. Whenever this antelope is suddenly startled, it utters a sharp, distinctive whistle. In places where many reedbucks are abroad, you can hear this whistle periodically throughout the night.

The Bohor Reedbuck, *Redunca redunca,* found throughout most of Africa, frequents plains, swamps, and mountain country but avoids heavy forests. Slenderer than the kob, it has also a shorter and bushier tail. The black, ridged horns, twelve to sixteen inches long, spread upward and outward with a forward curve at the tip.

The average height of the bohor at the shoulder is about thirty inches, and the general colour is yellowish red; it is among the largest of the nine different kinds of reedbucks.

A Mountain Antelope. The Grey or Vaal Rhebok, *Pelea capreolus*, is a close relative of the reedbuck. The vaal never enters the forest; instead, it lives in mountain passes and rocky glens in small family groups—an old male with five or six females and their young. Spending the day on the hilltops and descending to the lower plains to feed and drink, the vaal makes its way back soon after sunrise. This creature is possessed of boundless energy; it would be hopeless to try to overtake a vaal rhebok from below.

Projecting straight up from the head of the vaal are short, slender horns. Its ears are long and narrow, the tail moderately long and bushy. The somewhat woolly hair is pale grey, while the head and limbs are fawn coloured. Females are about twenty-eight inches high at the shoulder; males are two or three inches taller.

The vaal rhebok frequents the open hilly regions of South Africa.

SABLE AND ROAN ANTELOPES—
STRONG AND STATELY CREATURES

The Sable Antelope, *Hippotragus niger*, is the most stately, if not the most magnificent, of all the antelopes. Its only possible rival, said Theodore Roosevelt, is the greater kudu.

Unlike the deer and most other antelopes, the sable arches its neck when running—like the champion at the horse show. Though it can travel at a good clip if need be, it is not so fast as the wildebeest. Largely, though not entirely, a grass-eater, it favours thinly forested country where there is ample cover interspersed with open sunlit glades. Alarmed, it utters a series of snorts much like those of a horse. If wounded and cornered, the sable will fight savagely for its life.

——SUPERB HORNS. Both male and female sable antelopes are well armed—they have superb sickle-shaped horns sweeping backward from the face in an arc that may reach a length of sixty-four inches. The horns have extremely sharp points, and this courageous animal knows how to make effective use of them in defending itself from attack. About four and one-half feet at the shoulder, the sable weighs 450 pounds. It has large ears and an erect mane.

Females and young are reddish brown with considerable white about the muzzle and below the eyes. Becoming darker with maturity, the males are almost black by the time they grow up.

A STATUESQUE ANIMAL

Handsome and dignified, the sable antelope runs with its head drawn back, like a fine, spirited horse. It likes the company of the herd, in which it travels with from ten to eighty of its fellows. Notice the splendid sickle-shaped horns—they may extend to an impressive length of sixty-four inches.

The range of the sable antelope includes the Transvaal, Rhodesia, and the coast districts of East Africa, where it travels in herds of anywhere from ten to eighty—though groups of more than twenty are rare. Even in large herds there is only one adult bull. The old ones and the young competing males are not permitted to join the herd; instead, they associate in small bachelor groups.

The Roan Antelope, *Hippotragus equinus,* like the sable, can travel at a fast pace. Its gallop is rather heavy but strong and brisk, much like that of a horse. When it travels on hard ground, you can hear its hoofbeats for quite a distance.

Slightly larger than its cousin the sable antelope, the roan has considerably smaller horns—usually less than thirty inches long—and its ears are longer. The roan antelope stands almost five feet at the shoulder, weighing approximately 625 pounds. The male has a grizzled roan coat, very different from that of the bull sable antelope. The animal is a doughty fighter, as many a pack of wild dogs have discovered to their sorrow.

The roan favours rather open regions, usually upland, rolling country, not thickly wooded. In East Africa it goes up to an elevation of six thousand feet, but it does not care for higher altitudes. Primarily a grass-feeder, the roan will travel long distances away from water; when water is available, the animal drinks regularly about daybreak.

There are seven known types of roan antelope, and their combined range extends throughout the plains of Africa north of the Orange River.

ANTELOPES WITH STRAIGHT HORNS

GEMSBOKS—THEIR HORNS ARE DANGEROUS WEAPONS

The Gemsbok, *Oryx gazella*, may not be the fleetest antelope on the African veldt, but it requires an exceptionally fast horse to overtake one. When hard pressed or attacked, the gemsbok will boldly defend itself. Pursued by dogs, either domestic or wild, it will quickly turn on them.

The gemsbok has four-foot-long rapier-like horns that extend backward and upward from the head. Both sexes normally have horns, but those of females are longer. A gemsbok is fast as lightning with these sharp weapons. Natives report instances of lions found transfixed on the horns of the gemsbok.

Graceful Creatures. Gemsboks are sociable animals, frequenting open country. A herd of gemsboks trotting in single file is one of the most spectacular sights of Africa. They stride along in soldierly fashion, their long, slender horns gleaming like bared sabres in the sunlight as these animals whirl about in unison before coming to a stand.

The gemsboks cover the plains with an easy, swinging trot or gallop and seem to skim along with an effortless glide. When they walk, their heads nod with each step, as in the case of a horse. The author has watched the graceful creatures gallop away across the veldt. Singularly inconspicuous even in wide open spaces, they seem to disappear in the dancing mirages.

A gemsbok resembles a thoroughbred in its carriage and posture. Neat and compact in build, it has a level back and a short, horselike neck. The general colour is greyish brown with a black stripe extending along the lower sides of the body.

"BUILT-IN" SPEARS

The fierce-looking horns of the gemsbok may actually reach four feet in length. Well-endowed for fighting, the gemsbok can impale its enemies on its horns, and, at the same time, be protected against severe injury because of the unusually tough skin on its shoulders. Even the kingly lion or a savage pack of dogs can be held off by the gemsbok.

Gemsbok Babies. The young gemsbok is born early in the year. At birth, the calf's horns are nearly one inch long, bent backwards, and knobbed at the points. The newborn calf's hue is a pale reddish grey, growing paler as the youngster increases in size. Its mother keeps it hidden in the bush for several months, until about the time the calf begins to change colour; now it is ready to join the herd with her.

The gemsbok is one kind of a group of antelopes known as oryxes. Other oryxes are much like their big relative the gemsbok. The Beisa Oryx and the Fringe-Ear Oryx of East Africa have shorter horns than the gemsbok and lack the black flank stripes; otherwise the animals look much the same. The White Oryx inhabits the sun-baked deserts of North Africa; its horns are not straight, as in other oryxes, but curve strongly backwards.

The animal is often hunted by the Arabs.

ADDAXES—MADE FOR A LIFE IN THE DESERT

The Addax, *Addax nasomaculatus*, is a native of the desert regions of North Africa and the Sudan. This remarkable animal can go for months without water to drink; it also changes its colour seasonally from sandy or brownish grey to reddish brown.

The addax is very much like the oryx in appearance, except for its horns and feet. Both sexes have horns, measuring some forty inches along the curve, but in the female they are more slender and less spirally twisted than in the male. Broad, spreading feet are adaptations for support on soft, sandy wastes. The addax associates in pairs or small herds and travels far over the desert in the wake of thunderstorms, which bring up quick growths of green vegetation.

Like the white oryx, the addax is hunted by the Arabs, since it is a fairly sizeable creature; it has a shoulder height of about forty inches. A large patch of black hair marks the forehead, while below it is a streak of white stretched across the nose. The hind quarters, tail, and legs are white.

ANTELOPES WITH LONG FACES

HARTEBEESTS—FAST AND TIMID

Society-loving creatures, hartebeests (the name is simply South African Dutch for "hart beasts") often associate in large herds in Africa. Preferring open plains and desert areas, where they seem to live almost independent of water, they feed exclusively on grasses, usually during daylight hours. The hartebeest is of such a timid and retiring nature that it rarely attempts to defend itself, even when attacked or wounded.

A TIMOROUS CREATURE

Though the majestic hartebeest is one of the larger and faster antelopes, it shrinks from fighting. Even when it is attacked or hurt, it is too shy to retaliate. The fine figure of the hartebeest adorned ancient Roman coins, symbolizing the African holdings of the Empire.

Among the fastest of the larger antelopes, hartebeests move with a heavy gallop when first startled. Then they gain high speed as the apparent stiffness in the joints disappears and they vanish in a cloud of dust. When grazing, hartebeests seem to post a sentinel on a large ant-hill, where it has an extensive view of the surrounding bush-covered veldt. And well may they keep a careful lookout; their flesh is much relished by the natives and the lions.

The hartebeest dwells throughout most of Africa south of the Sahara. There are many kinds of hartebeest. The Korrigum, and its relatives the Senegal Hartebeest and the Topi, are fairly large antelopes with a dark, reddish-brown, narrow face. The Bubal Hartebeest, which stands about forty inches at the shoulder, has an abnormally long face. The Kongoni, one of the smaller hartebeests, is often seen in Kenya and Tanganyika. It is frequently shot for food. Both sexes of the hartebeest have ringed horns that are more or less lyre-shaped.

ANTELOPES ON THE WANE

Rather rare today are the Blesbok and the Bontebok, beautiful antelopes with fine, glossy coats. Their faces are long and narrow, and above them are rather short horns, heavily ringed and lyre-shaped, and curving slightly backward. Formerly widely spread over the northern plains of the Cape Colony, the Orange Free State, and the Transvaal, these creatures were extensively hunted in the past, so that we do not find them in many parts of their native South Africa at present.

The bontebok (its name means "spotted buck" in Dutch) wears a purplish-red coat, and has a white face and rump. The blesbok ("blaze buck") has a white blaze or spot on the forehead, but is otherwise not very different from the bontebok. Both are closely related to the Sassaby, a large antelope with short horns that spread upward and backward in a crescent-shaped curve, and all are cousins of the better-known hartebeest.

WILDEBEESTS OR GNUS—WITH HEADS LIKE THE BUFFALO'S

Black Wildebeests—Fast Trotters with Amazing Endurance. The Black Wildebeest, or White-tailed Gnu, *Connochaetes gnou*, with its long-faced, buffalo-like head, is not only one of the queerest-looking of the antelopes—it is a fascinating animal to observe as it moves fleetly along the African veldt. The wildebeests travel at a fast trotting pace, taking immense strides; they can keep this up for most of the day. Their call is curious, too—a loud, bellowing snort with a peculiar metallic ring.

When a herd is about to stop and have a look back, the leader, slowly cantering along, wheels around, followed by the herd in single file—but not until the last one has made the turn does the leader give the signal to pull up.

When a troop of wildebeests stop to face an intruder, it is not uncommon to see a pair of bulls or cows drop to their knees and start sparring furiously with each other for a minute or two.

Despite its habit of travelling a considerable distance to forage for fresh pastures where the grass is green, the wildebeest is really a home-lover. In all its wide range it has some particular spot where it goes the year round to rest during the warm midday hours. When feeding, the black wildebeest frequently kneels, a posture that few if any other animals assume.

The black wildebeest's name is not quite accurate, for it is dark brown—dark enough to be almost black. A fierce-looking creature rather horselike in build, it measures four feet at the shoulder—it is the smallest of the gnus. It has a long, flowing, bushy white tail, and an erect mane on the neck.

The horns, unringed, are directed downward, then abruptly upward in front of the face. A tuft of hair on the nose adds to its queer appearance.

Once common on the flatlands of South Africa, the black wildebeest used to be heavily hunted for its skin, and the animal has all but disappeared from the wild state. It is carefully preserved in the Cape Province.

Blue Wildebeests—Spectacular and Speedy. Like its relatives, the Brindled Gnu, or Blue Wildebeest, *Gorgon taurinus*, travels in herds. Today it is a much commoner animal than the black wildebeest.

In general appearance a troop of brindled gnus resemble a herd of bison—from a distance, at any rate—and the behaviour of both animals is very much alike. When stampeded, the gnus take off with a wild tossing of the head, combined with heel-kicking and tail-waving. At first they go into a fast trot, but after fifty yards or so they turn into an undulating gallop. There is much indignant snorting and grunting; their protests carry quite a distance.

In the long run the brindled gnu is one of the speediest animals—if not the fleetest of the lot—on the African veldt. On the gallop it frequently travels in single file, often making a most spectacular picture along the skyline.

Cornered or hard pressed, the gnu will charge; still, it almost always stops short of its objective, trying to appear much more ferocious than it really is.

——HERDS IN THE HUNDREDS. Brindled gnus travel in groups of anything from a dozen to several hundred. They frequent the open plains, where their favourite food is grass. Fast as these antelopes

[7-7]

A small antelope measuring only about 24 inches at the shoulder, the duiker gets its name, which means "diver", from the way it plunges headlong into underbrush and thickets. There are at least 20 different kinds of duikers ranging the length and breadth of Africa.

See page 798

The steinbok is even smaller than the duiker. One of the few African game animals not driven from its ancient range by civilization, the little antelope favours the scattered brush of the open plains. It generally remains inconspicuous during daylight hours, depending on its speed for safety should the need arise. See page 877

[7-7A]

Neat and compact in build but by far not the fleetest of African antelopes, the sociable gemsboks trot along in single file until, alerted, they
whirl in unison and take a stand. With four-foot-long rapier-like horns,
and as fast as lightning in utilizing this endowment of Nature, a gemsbok will boldly defend itself against all comers. *See page 805*

[7-8]

[7-8A]

Cornered or hard pressed, the gnu or wildebeest trying to appear much more ferocious than it really is, will charge—but it
almost always stops short of its objective. One of the swiftest
animals on the African veldt, the gnu's speed is not restricted to
short bursts; it can carry on at a long-stride fast trot or undulating gallop for the better part of a day. *See page 809*

THE BISON—WILD OX OF NORTH AMERICA

The bison mother bears a single calf, which she nurses and protects tenderly; the young one may remain with her until a new calf is born. Bison, for all their great bulk (they may weigh half a ton or more), are fleet-footed animals, capable of dashing across the plains at a speed of up to forty miles per hour. Once extremely abundant, they now survive mainly in national parks.

See page 779.

ARABIAN ORYXES—THEY DO WITHOUT WATER FOR LONG PERIODS

The handsome antelopes pictured above, known locally as "wudhyhiys", are quite scarce nowa-
days, and hunting them is prohibited by Saudi Arabian law. They inhabit one of the hottest and
driest parts of the world, yet desert life does not seem to inconvenience them. During the long
periods of excessive drought they manage to survive without any drinking water. *See page 807.*

are, some authorities believe that a brindled gnu can be overtaken by an exceptionally fleet horse. Dependent on a regular supply of water, wildebeests migrate from one drinking place to another.

THE GROTESQUE GNU

Strangest of the antelopes, both in appearance and behaviour, is the gnu or wildebeest, of Africa. It has a body like a horse, a long, melancholy face, bunches of hair on its neck and throat, and a bushy tail. This animal will often behave quite belligerently when aroused. It is a sharp-sighted creature, and very wary of man.

The brindled gnu is bigger than its black cousin—it measures four and one-half feet at the shoulder, and weighs up to 550 pounds. Brindled in colour, this gnu has brown stripes on the neck and shoulders; its tail is black. The smooth horns spread outward instead of forward. This animal dwells for the most part on the open plains of central and eastern Africa north of the Zambesi River.

Wildebeests mate from June onward. The cows separate from the bulls when the calves are born eight and one-half months later. Cows usually have one calf at a time.

EAL/7—E

GAZELLES AND THEIR RELATIVES

The Gazelle, *Gazella*, is a slender, beautifully formed small antelope with high-tension muscles that can send it hurtling across the barren wilderness at an incredible speed. Although it is among our most comely and graceful animals and lives in accessible and well-traversed regions, the gazelle has had surprisingly little mention in literature. No one seems to have made a detailed study of its life history.

WHERE THE GAZELLE LIVES

The gazelle is at home in the hottest and driest parts of the Old World.

It is a creature of the burning deserts, of the treeless plains and sandy wastes. That there is no water for miles and miles around, and not a vestige of shade in which to shelter itself from the torrid heat of the midsummer sun, does not inconvenience this lover of the great open spaces.

FLEETER THAN THE CHEETAH

The cheetah is perhaps the only mammal that can catch a gazelle in a straight run.

But this holds good only for the cheetah's first burst of speed—and even so, it must get within a reasonable distance before the race begins.

Arabs train the speedy Saker falcon to swoop down upon the gazelle and strike it a stunning blow on the head. This gives the hunters, on their fast horses, a chance to catch up. In Asia, the natives hunt the gazelle with gazelle hounds, but few dogs can be expected to match the speed of a full-grown gazelle. Both greyhound and falcon are employed in the capture of the gazelle, and in some cases both hawk and hound are trained to work together.

WHAT GAZELLES LOOK LIKE

We find sixty or so different kinds of gazelles in southern Asia and northern Africa. Most of these creatures of the stony plains or deserts are comparatively small, not more than about two or three feet at the shoulder. For the most part, they have lyre-shaped, ringed horns that curve backward and upward (they are generally larger in the male,

and the females of a number of species lack them). Their coat is sandy
brown in colour, which makes them inconspicuous in desert regions.
In many cases, the animals have black and white bands on the face
and flanks.

"GAZELLE BOYS"

Earlier in this book we mentioned some strange stories of children
who are said to have wandered off or been abducted and reared by
four-footed foster mothers. Stories of this nature have been told so
frequently that they have found a place in romantic literature and are
prominent in folklore.

None that has become known in our time has stood up under
scientific investigation.

One of the most amazing of these stories concerns a "gazelle boy"
—it got world-wide publicity in newspapers and magazines. It was in

SWIFT AS THE WIND

The delicate, sprightly gazelle is one of the fastest mammals on earth. None but the
cheetah, the greyhound, or the hawk can overtake or capture it. Gazelles are often found
on hot, burning deserts, where they live without water or shade near by; however, the
Tibetan gazelle, or goa, pictured above, prefers grassy plains.

September, 1946, that the newspapers carried headlines such as this one: "Fast Gazelle Boy Chased by Car for Two Hours." According to the newspaper account, native hunters on the Syrian steppes found a boy running wild with a herd of gazelles. To make it all the more convincing, there were pictures of a naked native boy, about fourteen; he looked like a perfectly healthy child.

Prince Fawaz el Shaalan, leader of a Transjordanian desert tribe, who captured the "gazelle boy", said: "We were hunting gazelles in the desert by car, when suddenly I saw a human form among these graceful beasts. I ordered my companions to cease firing and we pursued the form. Although we were in a car, it took two hours to catch up with the boy, who fell down exhausted.

"A physician who examined the boy at the Baghdad hospital said this child acts, eats, and cries like a gazelle, but there is no doubt that he is a human being who was brought up by the gazelles after having been abandoned by his mother."

A MYSTERY EXPLAINED

This might have gone down in history as another unexplained mystery. However, later investigation indicated that the boy, mentally deficient, was probably the son of a Bedouin family living in the neighbourhood.

Other "gazelle boys" subsequently turned up in Transjordan, Iraq, Syria, and Lebanon. In no case had these children actually been reared by animals. Still, many people readily accepted the tales about them.

GERENUKS—THEY STAND ON THEIR HIND LEGS

The Gerenuk, or Waller's Gazelle, *Litocranius walleri*, is noted for its ability to feed while standing on its hind legs. This it does frequently in order to reach the leaves on which it dines. It has a further adaptation for this form of eating—its extraordinarily lengthy slender neck, and legs that are very long for the size of its body.

The males carry twelve-inch horns that curve forward toward the tip and are heavily ringed. The general colour of the gerenuk is reddish brown, with a broad darker band down the middle of the back.

The typical gerenuk dwells in East Africa from Jubaland to Uganda and south to the Kilimanjaro district.

GOITRED GAZELLES—THEIR THROATS SWELL
AT MATING TIME

The Goitred Gazelle, *Gazella subgutturosa*, has a spectacular speed for an animal its size (about twenty-six inches at the shoulder). We have reason to suppose that in full flight the goitred gazelle can reach a speed of sixty miles per hour. It can run at an average of thirty miles per hour for a distance of ten miles, and it can easily pull ahead of a car doing forty miles per hour.

The latter part of this animal's scientific name was derived from the swollen condition of the male's throat during mating time.

The goitred gazelle wears a coat of very dark cinnamon, but most of the head is white or buffy white, while the tail is black. Usually only the male has horns—they curve backward with an upward swing; as in most gazelles, the horns are ringed. The females are hornless or almost so, with mere short stubs passing for horns.

Asia Minor to the Gobi Desert. The goitred gazelle is a desert-loving creature that associates in small herds. It has its home further north than any other of the typical gazelles. Its immense range extends from Asia Minor and the Caucasus through Russian Turkistan, Syria, Iran, and Afghanistan to the Altai Mountains and the Gobi Desert. Sometimes the animal is kept by the Arabs in tame herds.

SPRINGBOKS—THEY FLASH SIGNALS

The Springbok, *Antidorcas marsupialis*, derives its common name from its peculiar habit of leaping in the air at most unexpected times. It is gazelle-like in general form, with perfect lyre-shaped horns that curve inward evenly at the tip.

This gazelle stands about thirty inches at the shoulder and weighs from seventy to eighty pounds. Especially noteworthy about it is a fold of skin which it has on its back. When alarmed, the animal turns the fold inside out, displaying an array of white hairs. These hairs probably serve as a warning signal.

There was a time when the graceful springbok gathered in immence herds on the plains of South Africa north to the Orange River. Thousands used to be seen trekking in search of good forage, but persistent hunting has greatly reduced the numbers and range of the animals.

Good Samaritan. E. M. Menmuir gives us a picturesque account of an actual incident which shows the sympathetic feeling of a springbok for an unfortunate neighbour. It seems that while marooned in dune veldt south of the Kalahari, a lawyer and his wife heard a low, whimpering sound coming from the dunes. Presently a springbok showed up, followed by a wildebeest which was evidently in a bad way.

Apparently the springbok was leading the wildebeest, for every time the wildebeest made the whimpering sound the springbok would wait for it and then nose it gently along. Later it was found that the wildebeest was quite blind, evidently from the venom of a snakebite.

KLIPSPRINGERS—JUMPERS AND WHISTLERS

The Klipspringer, *Oreotragus oreotragus*, is a mountaineer that invariably is found on rocky slopes in Africa from the Cape of Good Hope to Ethiopia. An alert little creature, continually on the lookout for enemies, it trusts rather to seeing its enemy first than to escaping detection. When it is not unduly alarmed or when its curiosity is aroused, the klipspringer will utter a shrill whistle.

When disturbed, the klipspringer always retreats uphill, taking what advantage it can of bush and rocky cover. Reaching the summit, it will pause, silhouetted against the skyline, for a final backward look. Against the rocks and bush, its protective coloration makes the klipspringer almost imperceptible even when in full view.

The "African Chamois". The klipspringer's agility in its precipitous rocky home has earned for it the name of "African chamois". It can obtain a foothold on a very small rocky projection; when it is agitated, it fairly bounces up almost perpendicular cliffs like a rubber ball.

Though the klipspringer loves company, it is not gregarious; two or three often associate together, and sometimes as many as eight—but scarcely ever more—will maintain a group in a small area. They feed both by browsing on leaves and shoots of shrubs and by grazing on grass.

This dainty little animal is about twenty inches high at the shoulder. The horns of the bucks are ringed at the base and rise almost straight up from the head, bending only slightly forward. The females are generally hornless. As for the klipspringer's large, cylindrical hoofs, they are more like the feet of a mountain goat than those of an antelope. The hair, too, is peculiar, being long and brittle, with a pithy structure resembling deer hair. The klipspringer's general body colour is yellowish brown speckled with yellow. The animal makes an excellent pet, being very playful and fond of showing off its ability to jump.

ORIBIS—THEY HIDE IN TALL GRASS

The Oribi, *Ourebia ourebi*, the swiftest of the smaller antelopes, is as much at home in the rolling foothills as it is on the plains. When first disturbed, it takes off across the plains in a low, running gallop. At a safe distance, it springs into the air, each time coming down on its hind legs first.

Though the oribi wanders freely over the open plains, it is primarily a creature of tall grasses and bush country. Here it lies so close that it will almost permit itself to be stepped on, hoping to escape detection. When it does move, it goes with a tremendous rush, leaping in the air to see any danger that may be ahead.

A graceful creature, the oribi is yellowish brown in colour, and can generally be recognized by the long tufts or brushes on its knees. The male has straight, ringed horns, about six inches long, that project upright from the head.

In the bush the oribi lives in twos and threes, but on the open plains ten or twelve individuals may be seen feeding together. Alarmed, they disperse in all directions—there is no unity in the group.

The oribi's range extends from South Africa to Ethiopia.

STEINBOKS—ANTELOPE OF THE OPEN SPACES

The Steinbok, *Raphicerus campestris*, is one of the few African game animals that have persisted over much of their ancient range despite the encroachment of man. It lives either singly or in pairs and is never sociable.

The steinbok, as a rule, favours open plains broken by scattered bush.

Though it is at home on stony ground, it will never take to the mountains, nor has it been seen on steep hillsides. Passing the day hidden in tall grass, it comes out to feed during the evening and early morning hours. It is most conspicuous in the open spaces, where, for safety, it relies upon its ability to speed away. When hard pressed by dogs, however, it occasionally takes refuge in an aardvark burrow underground.

Not unlike the oribi in appearance, the steinbok has larger ears and a longer tail. Its body is sandy-reddish, with the head a darker shade; the shoulder height is about twenty-two inches and it weighs twenty-five pounds.

Generally found in the plains of South Africa, the steinbok ranges north to the Transvaal and Kenya.

GAZELLES ARE A GREAT RACE

The Old World has gazelles in such abundance that we cannot hope to look at all of them here. But a few more are definitely worth a passing glance. The Addra Gazelle, *Gazella dama*, also known as the *nanger*, *dama*, and *mhorr*, is the largest of the gazelles. It stands thirty-seven inches at the shoulder and has a longer neck than most gazelles, but its horns are rather short. Native to the desert regions of North Africa, it is easily recognized by the white rump patch which includes the tail.

Grant's Gazelle, one of the larger varieties, is the best-known gazelle found in East Africa. An attractive creature, it stands thirty-three inches at the shoulder and weighs 150 pounds. Both sexes have long, handsome, lyre-shaped horns which measure about thirty inches in the male, only seventeen in the female. This animal ranges from Tanganyika north through Kenya and Ethiopia, and travels in herds; often it is seen near water holes, in easy fellowship with other animals.

The Goa is a famous gazelle of the Asiatic plains, deserts and upland plateaux, where it sometimes falls victim to wolves. In India the Chinkara, or Indian Gazelles, are the best known and most widely spread of the gazelles. These fawn-coloured animals stand about two feet at the shoulder; they are much hunted with dogs and golden eagles.

The Atlas Gazelle is a small creature native to the higher ridges in Morocco, Algeria, and Tunisia, where it is known as the *admi* or *edmi*. Another small antelope, the Dorcas Gazelle, occupies the hot deserts and barren wastes of Palestine and Syria as well as the burning sands of North Africa to the Sudan and the Sahara.

The Rhim is the gazelle of the Libyan desert and the sand dunes of Algeria and the Sahara. Its colour is a very pale sandy, appearing almost white in the distance. The Korin is the Red-fronted Gazelle of Equatorial Africa, Senegal, the northern Cameroons, and the Sudan. Speke's Gazelle, a native of Somaliland, is peculiar in that it has a flabby corrugated elevation on its nose.

A gazelle fast approaching extinction is the Red Gazelle, of the Algerian Sahara.

Thomson's Gazelle, a small, graceful animal with well-developed white facial markings, and a narrow black band bordering the white on the sides of the rump, is familiar to every sportsman who visits Kenya and Tanganyika Territory.

Heuglin's Gazelle is another variety with sharply defined flank stripes.

DWARF ANTELOPES

The Royal Antelope, *Nesotragus pygmaeus*, is not only the smallest antelope in Africa but one of the smallest hoofed mammals in the whole world. Only ten inches at the shoulder, it has horns less than one inch long. This pygmy lives in the forests of the West African coastal region from Liberia to Nigeria. It has a close relative in another pygmy antelope—the Suni, *Nesotragus moschatus*. This attractive little animal of the forests of East Africa stands just about a foot at the shoulder.

The Dik-Dik, a tiny slender antelope not much bigger than the royal antelope or the suni, is about fourteen inches at the shoulder and weighs six or seven pounds. This handsome, harelike animal favours semi-arid brush country and, when disturbed, it bolts through the underbrush like a rabbit. Every year, thousands of dik-diks are captured in nets and killed for their skins, which are made into ladies' gloves. The animals are found in many parts of Africa.

OTHER INTERESTING ANTELOPES

Another interesting little creature is the Somali Beira, or Beira Antelope, a big-eared, greyish-fawn antelope with large feet bearing globular pads.

Its shoulder height is about twenty inches, and it weighs in the neighbourhood of twenty pounds. Its spike horns are four inches long. Beiras are scarce, but they may be seen in twos or fours in the arid mountain regions in the interior of Somaliland and Ethiopia. When they hear a disturbing sound, they will often leap on to a high rock and try to see whether there is any cause for alarm. If there is, they are off in a flash.

BLACKBUCKS—INDIA'S FLEETEST ANTELOPES

The Blackbuck, or Indian Antelope, *Antilope cervicapra*, is the fastest of India's antelopes—it can leave a pair of greyhounds far behind. Credited with a speed of fifty miles an hour, this handsome antelope can be overtaken by a cheetah only in that animal's first lightning-swift burst of speed. On one occasion a blackbuck was run down on horseback, but a very fast Arabian horse was used; this feat has not been repeated, so far as we know.

Herds of Ten to Thousands. Open plains are the favourite haunts of the blackbuck. These once-abundant animals travel in herds often

A STARTLING CONTRAST

The beautiful blackbuck or Indian antelope has a strikingly coloured coat—shiny black on top, pure white underneath. Twisted, ringed horns rise from its head in a broad "V"-shape. For many years, this animal was common game in India, and was widely hunted. Today, it has become so scarce that it has to be protected by law.

numbering from ten to thirty; but there are records of vast herds of several thousand of both sexes and all ages being seen together. The blackbuck never enters the forest or tall grass country. A grazing animal, it feeds on short grasses; often it lives in regions where it is impossible to obtain water.

Occasionally the blackbuck roams across cultivated land, doing damage to the crops. Should the antelope be startled, it will leap high into the air again and again. Then away it speeds, displaying the fleetness of foot for which it is famous.

Blackbuck Horns. The blackbuck is readily distinguished from all other antelopes by its beautiful horns; ringed and spirally twisted, they spread out from the top of the head in the form of a broad "V". The record horn length is twenty-nine inches.

As a rule only males have horns—occasionally an old female will be the exception.

Adult bucks are black or blackish brown, while the females and young are reddish fawn in colour. Standing thirty-two inches at the shoulder, the blackbuck weighs about eighty-five pounds. As we have noted, this splendid creature is the only "true" antelope—at least according to its scientific name. It is the common medium-sized antelope of India.

IMPALAS—CHAMPION HIGH-JUMPERS

The Impala, or Pallah, *Aepyceros melampus*, is one of the most graceful of a race of graceful creatures. The cover in which the impala lives is sometimes dense; more often the animal sticks to parklike country, where it can feed in open glades. It always chooses an area where water is close at hand. During the heat of the day it rests in the shade of trees, usually lying down.

The impala is a great traveller; nomadic in habits, it usually travels along river courses. When a herd is alarmed, the animals bound off, sailing over the bushes and rocks with little apparent effort, and disappear in the recesses of the forest. In jumping, the impala seems to float through the air in graceful undulations very different from the springlike action of most antelopes.

For a limited distance the impala is perhaps the fleetest of all antelopes—not only does it bound over bushes and rocks, but often over its companions as well. One observer saw an impala cover a horizontal distance of seventy feet in three successive leaps—one leap alone measured thirty-five feet. The impala has been known to clear an eight-foot wire fence. It is easy to approach these unsuspicious creatures —unless they have become wary from frequent persecution.

AN AMAZING LEAPER

Famous for its high jumps over rocks and bushes, the impala easily vaults over an eight-foot barrier. When it takes off, this nimble creature soars through the air with the grace of a bird, rather than like a hoofed animal.

An impala herd on the run presents a graceful and eye-filling picture. Although the animals love company, they rarely gather in herds of more than fifty. Both sexes live together in the winter months, when the herds are at their largest. In the summer, they travel fair afield and live in scattered bands of one young male with fifteen or twenty ewes. He may have to fight for his harem from time to time, but is generally able to withstand the attacks of older bucks.

The impala's coat is reddish gold, the under-parts are white. Only the bucks have horns—ringed and lyre-shaped, they measure fourteen to twenty inches in length. The animal stands about three feet at the shoulder and weighs up to 160 pounds. The impala, although often the victim of packs of wild dogs and other flesh-eaters, is still found throughout much of its former range in Kenya Colony and Tanganyika, with a related form in South-West Africa and Angola.

DIBATAGS—ANTELOPE ODDITIES OF SOMALILAND

The Dibatag, *Ammodorcas clarkei*, is also called Clarke's gazelle, after the Westerner who discovered it in 1890. This strange-looking antelope has a very long neck and legs, and a thin, lengthy tail tipped with black. The animal stands three feet at the shoulder and wears a coat deep cinnamon in colour; it has white marking on its face.

A swift creature, the dibatag has a curious way of running. Neck and tail work like scissors when the dibatag speeds along: the head is repeatedly swung well back, then forward, and at the same time the tail is arched forward, then back. Apparently it was for this habit that the creature was named—dibatag means "tail raising" in Somali.

Only the male dibatag has horns—they measure about twelve inches in length and project upward and forward; ringed on the lower portion, they resemble the horns of a reedbuck.

The dibatag is a fairly rare antelope, living in small family groups among the parched sands of central Somaliland. It does not appear to require water, but depends upon plant food for its liquid.

Goat Antelopes—Neither Goats Nor Antelopes

THE GOAT ANTELOPES—the Rocky Mountain goat, the chamois, the musk ox, and their relatives—share in varying degrees the features which we find in goats and antelopes. Yet they are neither of these, and so we place them in a group by themselves.

Some of the goat antelopes enjoy living in more or less splendid isolation on remote mountain crags, at dizzying heights which sometimes range up to eighteen thousand feet. Others dwell in dense mountain forests, also at considerable elevations.

The thick-haired hides of the goat antelopes protect them from the rigours of the freezing temperatures that prevail in their favourite haunts. And, too, their hoofs are generally adapted in some way to give them the extra-sure footing without which they would soon perish. The animals are cud-chewers, and belong in the same family (Bovidae) as the oxen, true antelopes, true goats, and the sheep.

ROCKY MOUNTAIN GOATS—AT HOME ON PERILOUS PEAKS

The Rocky Mountain Goat, *Oreamnos americanus*, with its white coat and slender, backward-curving horns, looks for all the world like a true goat, yet it is a closer relative of Europe's chamois. A hardy creature, it is very much at home among the rugged cliffs and mountain peaks high above the timber line; not even the icy blasts of winter can induce it to seek the shelter of friendly woods.

From broken crags and treacherous mountain ledges the Rocky Mountain goat complacently views the world beneath. It never hastens its pace—in fact, it has no need of haste, for few natural enemies can follow the steep trail where the mountain goat picks its sure-footed way, as it forages for the foliage, moss, lichens, and other plants on which it feeds.

UNEXCELLED FOR VALOUR

This goat antelope can guard itself against almost any manner of four-footed foe. Sometimes the cougar, golden eagle, wolf, or bear may attack it, but then, too, even the great grizzly bear has appeared on the list of animals the Rocky Mountain goat has slain.

Arthur B. Fenwick, a field naturalist, gives amazing proof of the mountain goat's unexcelled valour: "A goat will sometimes kill a full-grown silvertip (grizzly) bear. I once found a big goat dead, which evidently had been killed by a silvertip, as there were lots of tracks all around, and the goat's back was broken. I thought it queer that the bear had not taken the goat away and buried it, as usual, so I

MISNAMED A GOAT

The goat antelopes are a separate group of animals, possessing traits found in both goats and antelopes. The Rocky Mountain goat, shown above, is a member of this group—it is not really a goat at all. Yet, like the goats, it is a superb climber, able to scale steep crags and dangerous precipices.

looked around. I found a large silvertip bear dead, and all bloated up; and when I examined him, I found that the goat had punched him twice, just back of the heart. He had been able to kill the goat, and had then gone off and died."

A Frightened Mountain Goat. The same writer tells of the only time he ever saw a mountain goat really frightened:

". . . When near the summit of a mountain in British Columbia a bear passed through a little pass near a pinnacle of bare rock, about two hundred feet high. He frightened an old long-bearded billy-goat, who immediately started up the pinnacle as hard as he could go and climbed near to its summit. And there the old fellow stood, or rather hung, in a most ridiculous attitude. His front feet were hooked over the eastern edge of the point, like a man looking over the peak of a steep house-roof, and holding only by his hands. His body and hind legs were well down the other side of the pinnacle, and completely overhung a frightful precipice."

The goat, however, never lost its hold, according to Fenwick. When the menace had passed, the animal made its way to safety.

THE MOUNTAIN GOAT'S WORST ENEMY

Nature itself is the most dreaded enemy of the Rocky Mountain goat. Spring thaws bring engulfing cataracts of snow and rock slides; winter storms may build masses of snow twenty feet deep that crash down the mountainside and envelop everything in their path. When the first thundering roar of an avalanche breaks the silence of the desolate wastes, the Rocky Mountain goat moves into action and climbs steadily upward to safety at the top of the nearest peak.

ROCKY MOUNTAIN GOAT FAMILIES

We know little about the breeding habits of the mountain goat; humans seldom venture into its cold and bleak haunts during the breeding season in November. In April or May one or two kids come into the world.

A kid that was born in captivity weighed seven and one-half pounds two days after birth, and measured thirteen and one-half inches at the shoulder.

SYMPHONY IN BLACK AND WHITE

White except for the black hoofs and ebony daggerlike horns which measure about 10 inches in length, the stout-legged Rocky Mountain goat inhabits the higher elevations of western North America from central Washington and Idaho to southern Alaska. Full-grown males stand 35 to 40 inches at the shoulder and weigh between 150 and 300 pounds; the females are slightly smaller but both sexes have horns and beards. Numerous and distinctly different species of the goat antelope family are found in all of the earth's great rugged mountain ranges. *See page 824.*

A HARDY ANIMAL WITH A DELICATE APPETITE

The Rocky Mountain bighorn sheep seldom if ever browses on shrubs—it prefers sweet, fresh mountain grasses and flowers. Grazing in upland meadows and on grassy hillsides above the timber line, the bighorn relies on its exceptionally keen eyesight and long-range vision for protection. Its feet are equipped with soft elastic pads which not only act as shock-absorbers but provide an effective grip on the precipitous cliffs of its homeland. Most spectacular of American wild sheep, the bighorn has very close relatives in Siberia. *See page 824.*

The "billies" or males are usually seen in twos and threes; if there are several goats in a group, they are generally "nannies" and kids. However, both parents may remain together while the young are very small; this is all to the good, as there is some danger that one of the babies may be stolen in an unguarded moment by a golden eagle.

SYMPHONY IN WHITE AND BLACK

The mountain goat is white except for the black hoofs and the ebony daggerlike horns, which measure ten inches in length. A stout-legged creature, the mountain goat has shoulders that are higher than the rump, giving it a hunchback appearance; some of the early pioneers referred to this shaggy creature as a small white mountain buffalo.

A full-grown male mountain goat stands between thirty-five and forty inches at the shoulder and weighs from 150 to three hundred pounds. The females are smaller than the males, but both sexes are horned and bearded.

There are four named forms: the Cascade Mountain Goat, the Alaska Mountain Goat, the Columbian Mountain Goat, and the Montana Mountain Goat. As you can gather from these names, the home range of the mountain goat covers the peaks of western North America from central Washington State and Idaho north-west to southern Alaska. Although the animal is not difficult to hunt once the sportsman gets within range of it, the rugged and remote nature of its homeland will apparently vouch for its survival indefinitely.

CHIRUS—HEAVY COATS FOR COLD CLIMATE

The Chiru, or Tibetan Antelope, *Pantholops hodgsoni*, is native to the plateau of Tibet; here, at elevations of twelve thousand to eighteen thousand feet, this robust goat antelope wanders about on its sharp-pointed hoofs. As an adaptation to a cold climate, the chiru has a very thick, full coat of erect hair, pale fawn in colour, that is woolly next to the skin. Peculiar swellings on each side of the animal's muzzle may serve as some sort of air conditioner—the animal certainly has need of one in the icy Tibetan winter months.

The female chiru is hornless, but the buck has horns that are black and ringed; with a two-foot maximum length, the horns bend forward slightly and away from each other. When seen in profile, the chiru's horns suggest a one-horned animal; the chiru is classed as one of the creatures that may have given rise to belief in the fabled unicorn.

IT WEARS A THICK WOOLLY SWEATER UNDER ITS COAT

At elevations of twelve to eighteen thousand feet, the chiru or Tibetan antelope needs maximum protection against the icy temperatures. Such protection is provided by its soft, extra-warm coat. The coat is smooth on the surface, but underneath, next to the skin, it is made up of densely enmeshed fine hair which traps the air and keeps it warm.

The Unsociable Chiru. The chiru keeps to the plains or open valleys, usually hiding during the day in hollows on the flats. Formerly groups of several hundred were not uncommon, but now herds consist of only a few individuals. The chiru mates in winter, and a single baby is born six months later. Except during the mating season, the sexes live apart. The animal stands about thirty-two inches at the shoulder, and weighs up to 120 pounds.

SAIGAS—GOAT ANTELOPE ODDITIES

The Saiga, *Saiga tatarica*, is the strangest looking of all the goat antelopes. This horned, sheeplike creature runs with lowered head, like a sheep or ox; its enormously swollen nose strongly suggests the moose. It is thirty inches tall at the shoulder but has fairly short legs.

Dust Filters. The saiga lives on alkali flats and vast stretches of open steppe country in central Asia, where it encounters severe dust and sand storms. As in the chiru, the many small hair-lined channels in the muzzle doubtless serve to filter the particles of dust and sand from the air which the animal breathes, and warm the air during the cold months. During the summer the harsh, thick hair is dull sandy-yellow in colour; in winter it becomes almost white, reminding us very much of a sheep's coat.

Bootleg Horns. Only the male saiga bear horns. Slightly lyre shaped in form, ringed in front, and pale amber in colour, they are only about half as long as the chiru's. Still, they are in great demand among the Chinese for "medicine". Despite rigid controls imposed by the Russians, there is considerable bootleg trade carried on in saiga horns, since they have been valued at 250 dollars a pair.

THE SAIGA HAS A HIGHLY SPECIALIZED NOSE

The saiga's homeland is the wide, open plains of central Asia, severely cold in winter, harsh and dusty in summer. One of Nature's marvellous adaptations for life in such a setting is the saiga's ugly, bulging nose. It has many small channels which warm the air before it goes into the lungs, and the animal's nostrils are lined with tiny hairs to filter out the dust. The wary saiga is considered a most difficult creature to stalk.

Formerly the saiga ranged from Poland and the Kalmuk steppe of southern Russia to the Gobi Desert, and, in the early days, the Kirghiz tribesmen trained golden eagles to catch the saiga as well as the gazelle and the wolf. Today the saiga is more or less limited to the desolate wastes north of the Aral Sea, and a small herd exists under government protection on an island in the Aral Sea.

STRANGE HUNT

If the saiga is a strange animal, the people in its homeland are equally strange, at least by our standards. Once the author travelled in Russian Turkistan to collect a group of saiga for the American Museum of Natural History. His caravan travelled some two hundred miles across steppe and desert, and still there was no news of saiga. The Russian official who accompanied the expedition was not inclined to see its purpose frustrated. Highhandedly he arrested a wealthy Kirghiz nomad and sent him off under guard with instructions to bring back an experienced saiga hunter, "or else".

Five days later, the captive returned with a fierce-looking barbarian in tattered clothing. The newcomer was riding a shaggy desert pony and carried a long, old-fashioned gun with a forked stick that served as a gun rest. This cagey stranger never allowed the party to get a glimpse of the saiga—apparently the animal was to be his prey alone. Somehow, one day, he managed to steal away in the early morning. Later, he returned. There was a satisfied expression on his face as he pointed to the dead beasts slung on his horse—one fine male, a female, and several half-grown saigas.

GORALS—WITH VALUABLE BONES

The Goral, *Naemorhedus*, which ranges from the Himalayas to eastern Siberia, is at home on grassy slopes as well as scrub forests and rocky mountainsides, at altitudes of three thousand to nine thousand feet. It is highly esteemed by the natives, who snare the animal for its bones; these, like the saiga's horns, bring a high price for use as "medicine" in the Chinese markets.

This "chamois of Asia" is not so big as its European cousin. A stocky, goatlike animal (it stands twenty-eight inches at the shoulder and weighs about sixty pounds), the goral wears a coarse coat of grey or brown, and its short horns curve slightly to the rear. The animal is not easily seen in the tall grass; when alarmed, it makes a rather penetrating hissing noise which may be heard in places where there is no other sign of the goral's presence.

ITS BONES ARE USED IN QUACK MEDICINES

In Asia, there is a primitive belief that the goral's bones hold special medicinal powers. Handsome prices are paid for these parts, providing incentive for natives to hunt the animals. Observers say that the goral plays a clever hiding game on grassy slopes.

SEROWS—"CLIFF DONKEYS"

The Serow, *Capricornis sumatraensis*, is larger and stockier than the goral, often attaining a weight of two hundred pounds. To find this creature, you must make a stiff climb to the steep cliffs and rugged crags three thousand or more feet above the plains. In fact, the serow has been found at elevations of thirteen thousand feet.

Even after such an arduous climb, it is still far from easy to trace the serow. After days and days of stalking, a hunter may be rewarded by nothing more substantial than a loud, angry, shrill, whistling snort in the thick bush and a momentary flash of the beast as it makes off through the thickets, covering fifteen or twenty feet at a bound.

The Chinese native name for the serow is *Ngai lii-tze*, meaning "cliff donkey"—a reference to its long ears and love for rugged country. During the rutting season, the rams have a habit of horning trees; this accounts for the smooth surface of the horns. Pursued by dogs, a ram will put up a terrific battle, unhesitatingly attacking man when cornered. The serow takes readily to water and can swim well. Chinese fishermen have seen this animal breasting the waters of the broad Yangtze.

THE DONKEY-EARED SEROW

An elusive animal, the stocky serow of East Asia lives on steep, bushy cliffs, at extremely high elevations, and is almost never seen by man. When tracked down and wounded, it may charge and become a serious menace. Natives call the serow "cliff donkey"— an apt name for this rock-climber with the big ears.

More or less solitary in their habits, the serows generally frequent the forestlands on the mountain slopes of northern India, Burma, southern and western China, Formosa, and Japan. In some places they have reddish coats, in others blackish-brown.

CHAMOIS—PRIZED QUARRY OF THE HUNTER

The Chamois, or Gems, *Rupicapra rupicapra*, is a goatlike mountain dweller found high above the timber line. An elusive, swift-footed small creature, it is one of the most difficult of animals to come to close quarters with. It is with no small pride that the Swiss or Austrian hunter wears on his hat a tassel of hairs taken from the chamois.

CHAMOIS SKIM LIKE BIRDS

A band of chamois, disturbed by hunters, need no path or ridge to follow. They skim like birds over wide ravines and dizzy peaks; their dainty feet have cup-shaped depressions which enable the animals to

AN ELUSIVE QUARRY

The chamois, a popular sport animal of the Alps, is no easy creature to kill. Its extra-ordinary feet, with their special gripping action, enable it to make high leaps and to land safely on treacherous mountain ledges. A broad jump of twenty feet is no record for the chamois. It is extensively hunted for its tasty flesh and valuable hide.

shoot down rocky chimneys and come to rest on tiny ledges no bigger than a man's hand. In winter the chamois leaves the cold, bleak heights to take refuge in lowland woods and sheltered valleys.

More slender than the sheep and the average goat, the chamois is easily recognized by its horns. Round and short, the horns rise perpendicularly from the head, and the tips are hooked abruptly backward and downward. Both males and females are horned.

In summer the chamois wears a coat that is soft tawny in colour; in winter, it changes to blackish brown. Males are larger than females, and may reach a shoulder height of thirty-two inches, and a weight of sixty-five pounds; females weigh about forty-five pounds. Formerly the soft, pliant leather known as "shammy" was made from the hide of the chamois; today the sheep and the goat are the common source of this product.

Though the typical chamois dwells in the Alps, local varieties range west over the Apennines and east through the Carpathians and the northern parts of the Balkan peninsula to the Caucasus and Asia Minor.

THE TAKIN—A RARE ANIMAL

The Takin, *Budorcas taxicolor*, is a rare animal, and little known. Living in exceedingly rough mountainous country from Bhutan to southern Shensi province in China, at elevations of eight thousand to fourteen thousand feet, the takin makes elusive prey in the dense thickets of bamboo and brush that are its home.

The Takin's Habits. From hunters we get a few interesting facts about the takin's habits. A heavy, clumsy animal, with a shaggy coat of yellowish hair, it spends the daytime in the thickets of rhododendron and bamboo near the timber line, leaving its shelter in the evening and early morning to graze on nearby grassy slopes. Breaking narrow trails through the bush, it follows them regularly to favourite feeding grounds and salt licks. To the Chinese, the animal is *yeh niu*, meaning "wild cattle". They trap the takin for its flesh, using dead falls, spear traps, and snares. When the natives approach a herd they do so with great caution, claiming that if one beast is wounded, the rest will charge the hunter, and that they may also charge without even this degree of provocation.

Very shy and secretive, the takin associates in small groups of two to eight. (A related species, the Golden Takin, travels in larger herds.) When alarmed, the takin gives a hoarse warning cough; but during the rut in July and August, bulls utter a loud bellow. The calves are born in March, and three days after birth they are able to follow their mother around.

SHYEST OF THE LOT

Least known of the goat antelopes is the takin. It lives in nearly impenetrable mountains, where steady rains and short supplies make tracking it down quite difficult. In addition, the takin is furtive, spending its days in dense thickets, well hidden from the eyes of man. Only a few specimens have ever been captured.

Seen from the side, the takin, with its curving horns, looks much like a wildebeest. It stands well over three feet at the shoulder, with front legs that are especially stout. A short face and thick muzzle are characteristic of the head, which the takin carries low, in oxlike fashion.

MUSK OXEN—GOAT ANTELOPES OF THE ARCTIC

The Musk Ox, Polar Ox, or Sheep Cow, *Ovibos moschatus*, a native of the barren wastes of the American Arctic, is not an ox at all, but a near relative of the takin of eastern Asia and the chamois of Europe. Although its legs are short, this robust, shaggy beast can gallop along at a fair speed, and in fact travels faster than a man; however, a dog can easily overtake a musk ox.

Herds of twenty or thirty musk oxen, chiefly cows and calves, are by no means unusual. The musk ox is one of the few animals that will join forces to combat a common foe. It would be useless for the animals to attempt to scatter and run away from a pack of swift Arctic wolves; by uniting in a circle with the calves safely inside, the musk oxen present an impregnable front to the enemy.

Still, it is not always possible to maintain an unbroken defensive position; sometimes three or four bulls will charge in unison in an effort to smash an attack.

With its back to a cliff and its two-foot-long horns ready for action, a single musk ox can protect itself from a whole pack of dogs or wolves.

MAN *versus* MUSK OX

Musk oxen often take to the water. The author once saw a herd of thirty musk oxen, including cows and many small calves, swim across a deep lake a mile wide near the Thelon River in the Canadian Northwest Territory.

They entered the water of their own accord and, strangely enough, at a spot where the author's plane was parked.

On the other hand, an old bull that the author cornered on a narrow, elevated peninsula jutting out into the lake, turned to face him rather than jump fifteen feet down into the water. Repeatedly the beast rubbed his nose on his front feet just above the ankles. Somehow this action seemed to stimulate his courage.

When the author got within twenty feet of the animal, down went the creature's head for a determined charge. The writer had just a split second in which to leap over the edge, landing in the icy water himself—much to the amusement of his companions.

A HEAVY COAT FOR SUB-ZERO WEATHER

Somewhat resembling a shaggy domestic bull in appearance, the musk ox is clothed in long, flowing chocolate-brown hair that falls almost to the fetlocks. A thick growth of wool underlies the heavy outer covering of hair and serves as an impenetrable blanket against sub-zero Arctic temperatures. Broad-spreading main hoofs and well-developed side hoofs have hair between them to facilitate progress on slippery ice or frozen snow. The tail is small and almost lost in the long hair of the rump.

A CASE OF MISTAKEN IDENTITY
The musk ox is not an ox, nor does it have musk glands like the musk deer, whose secretion furnishes the foundation for certain perfumes. The animal is, rather, a goat antelope, with horns somewhat resembling the takin's. A musky odour does emanate from the animal during its rutting season, however, and its flesh has a musky flavour at this time.

Both sexes have horns—massive structures that cover the head like a shield. Broad at the base and rising close together on top of the head, the horns curve downward along the side of the face behind the eyes, then upward to a sharply tapered point. The adult male is larger than the female—he generally measures about four feet at the shoulder, and weighs from seven hundred to nine hundred pounds.

In its frigid homeland, the musk ox roams far beyond the northern timber line. Its range extends from the coastal regions of northern Greenland south to the Thelon River, in north-eastern Canada, including the adjoining Arctic islands. There are three named geographical forms: the Black-faced Musk Ox, the Hudson Bay Musk Ox, and the White-faced Musk Ox.

The animal was once much preyed upon by the Eskimos, but now enjoys protection in Canada.

MUSKY ODOUR AT MATING TIME

The musk ox does not have specialized musk glands, but there is a noticeably musky odour about the animal during the rutting season, and the flesh has a decidedly musky taste.

Mating takes place between July and September, probably from late July into early August. Although the calves are usually born about May, some come as late as July and others early in March. One calf at a time is common, although occasionally twins are born. A new born calf stands eighteen inches at the shoulder and weighs sixteen pounds.

The musk ox feeds on grass, moss, and any other edible plants, including shoots of willows and even branches of scrub pine trees. In summer, luxuriant grass grows knee deep on the Barrens. Food is plentiful, and the musk ox waxes fat and contented, but in winter-time it must dig out a sparse livelihood of mosses and dead grass from under the driven snow.

Goats and Sheep in the Wild

IT IS NOT always an easy matter to tell the goats from the sheep, in the wild. Both are mountain folk, dwelling in the high places of the earth. Both are chewers of the cud, wear hairy coats, and possess hollow horns. But, although we may occasionally confuse a number of these creatures, there are some marked ways in which sheep and goats differ.

The wild goat is generally a more sure-footed and adventurous animal than the wild sheep. It can live off the coarsest of food. Although it may browse and graze on grassy slopes, it will, after eating, retreat to a high crag for safety and slumber. The goat's horns are directed backward and upward, while the sheep's horns are usually spirally curved. Most male goats have a distinct beard and a strong goaty odour. Both sheep and goats were domesticated before 3,000 B.C., and probably much earlier than cattle.

Wild goats are restricted to Europe, Central Asia, and North Africa. We find the wild sheep in the Northern Hemisphere, including North Africa. (Goats and sheep form a subfamily of the Bovidae.) The Rocky Mountain Bighorn Sheep, the most spectacular animal of the American group, is not entirely a creature of the New World; close relatives do occur in Siberia.

YIELD OF THE GOATS: MILK, MEAT, AND MOHAIR

Goats produce milk, butter, cheese, and flesh for food, and they have been doing so for a long time. There are many mentions of the goat in the Bible. Job's he-goats are said to have been so strong that they could overpower wolves, while some carried bears on their horns. The water and wine containers mentioned in the Bible were made of goatskin.

In Palestine the goats were driven daily to market and milked at the door of prospective customers. They were much used in sacrifices and feasts; even today, when an Arab chieftain receives a guest, a kid is immediately killed and prepared for serving.

Like the wool of the sheep, goat hair is used for clothing. It is from Angora goats that we get the famous mohair. Reluctant though the Turks were to part with their monopoly of this species, it is now bred extensively in South Africa and Australia, where it produces an even finer grade of mohair than it did at home.

The cashmere goat is famed the world over for its fine fleece; a short-legged, graceful but frugal creature able to subsist on little food, the cashmere goat was originally a native of the Vale of Kashmir and the forbidding mountain ranges of the impenetrable Himalayas. Cashmere, the famous cloth, and shawls made from it, were prized as far back as the time of the Roman Caesars. This rare yarn of Kashmir was once only for kings and their courts.

Today little cashmere actually comes from Kashmir—most of the better grades are products of China, Mongolia, and Tibet. It is combed out of the animal's coat.

SOME IMPORTANT WILD GOATS

THE TYPICAL BEARDED IBEX

Agile and Sure Footed. The Ibex, *Capra*, a native of Asia, North Africa, and Europe, is a common wild goat of the Old World. It dwells in the vicinity of precipitous cliffs and mountain crags at high elevations close to the snow line at all seasons of the year. Even in winter it does not resort to the shelter of timber; instead, it haunts steep hillsides where the snow is not deep.

A STURDY GOAT WITH FINE CURVED HORNS

Of all the wild goats, the ibex is probably the most familiar. This animal has almost disappeared in the Alps, where it was once fairly common; only a few small herds survive under the protection of the Italian government. The ibex may be tamed, and one species in Asia is said to be the ancestor of our domestic goat.

The ibex has acute senses of sight, hearing, and smell. Usually one animal seems to act as a lone sentry, keeping watch for possible danger; it utters a shrill warning whistle to alert its fellows at the slightest suspicion of anything untoward. Extremely agile and sure footed, the ibex can leap down a forty-foot precipice to a rocky ledge below with perfect control and almost insufferable calmness. Wild dogs and snow leopards are common enemies of this animal in the Himalayas.

Mating Time. October is the mating season, when the males descend from their lofty pinnacles and join the females. Both sexes herd together at this time of the year but disperse when the snow melts in the spring. The males retreat to the more inaccessible mountain crests, while the females remain behind to give birth to their one or two offspring during May or June.

What the Ibex Looks Like. The ibex is the typical bearded goat. Its enormous horns (they measure up to fifty-eight inches) rise close together on top of the head and sweep back in a wide, even arc, like the blade of a scimitar. In the true ibex the horns are heavily corrugated on the broad front. The animal has a coat of rather long loose hair, usually yellowish brown in colour.

Among the many kinds of these hardy animals, the Siberian Ibex, *Capra sibirica*, is the largest and most handsome; it is native to the mountains of central Asia, the Tien Shan, Altai, and the Himalayas. The Abyssinian Ibex is a stocky, heavily built species with short, stout horns, while the Nubian Ibex from upper Egypt, Arabia, Palestine, and upper Nubia can be recognized by its long, slender horns.

The European Ibex or Steinbok is now extinct in the wild. It formerly ranged in the higher Alps of Switzerland, Savoy and the Tyrol. A few still survive under protection on the Italian side of Monte Rosa. This animal is easily tamed but remains for ever capricious—a word, we might remember, that was originally applied to the goat.

ANCESTOR OF OUR DOMESTIC GOATS

The Chetan Ibex, Pasang, or Wild Goat, *Capra hircus*, is the source of bezoar, once famous as a reputed antidote for poison. To this day bezoar is still regarded in Iran as a remedy for many diseases. The substance is secreted in the stomach of the pasang, which is why the great systematizer Linnaeus called this goat *Capra bezoartica*.

Bezoar balls are found in the stomachs of other animals, especially those that lick their coats—cattle and gazelles, for example. A bezoar ball is usually round, and smaller than a golf ball. Generally a formation of lime and magnesium phosphate around some foreign substance, it often consists entirely of hair or vegetable fibre. Sometimes it is used as a pigment.

The domestic goat is a lineal descendant of the pasang, which roams in herds over barren, rocky hills. The pasang has the peculiar habit of selecting the narrowest of pinnacles on which to balance itself. This goat dwells in a territory that ranges from south-eastern Europe to south-western Asia, and includes the neighbouring islands.

The Spanish Wild Goat, *Capra pyrenaica*, used to be found through-out the mountains of the Iberian peninsula and is still plentiful in some parts of its former range. It is often referred to as the Pyrenean Ibex.

The horns are of the wild goat type, compressed and having a sharp inner edge in front instead of being broad and knotty as are those of the ibex.

LINK BETWEEN GOATS AND SHEEP

The Eastern Tur, or Caucasian Bharal, *Capra caucasica*, is a robust and handsome wild goat with comparatively smooth, short horns which curve outward and backward close to the neck. One form, Pallas's Tur, which also lives in the Caucasus Mountains, is closely related to the Asiatic Blue Sheep, or Himalayan Bharal, mentioned later. Thus Pallas's tur is in effect a connecting link between the sheep and the goats, but it is a goat and not a sheep.

The Western Tur, native to the western half of the main Caucasian range, while still a wild goat, has heavy bosses in front of the horns like a true ibex, but the horns are shorter, heavier and not so evenly arched. The turs like to spend their time on lofty precipices above the snow line.

BEARDLESS GOATS

The Himalayan Tahr, *Hemitragus jemlaicus*, is a beardless goat with short, evenly curved horns, that lives at high elevations in the Himalayas. Here it runs in herds of five to about twenty-five, among the crags and rocky precipices near the timber line; old males may even enter thick timber.

The tahrs are wary and sharp sighted; like all goats, they are nimble on a steep terrain.

Though the Himalayan tahr is rather sociable, the sexes normally

[7-9]

Never aggressive and reluctant to defend themselves even when attacked or wounded, the hartebeests apparently post a sentinel while they graze. Ranging in large herds throughout most of Africa south of the Sahara, hartebeests seem to live almost independent of water, feeding exclusively on grasses in the open plains and desert areas. *See page 807*

The nomadic impala feeds in the open glades of parklike country always with water close at hand. Whereas most African antelopes jump with a springlike action, the impala seems to float through the air in graceful undulations with little apparent effort. *See page 821*

[7-9A]

Most abundant of the antelope family are the gazelles, not only in number but in variety. Thomson's gazelle is a delicate, graceful animal native to Kenya and Tanganyika.
See *page 819*

[7-10]

The Dorcas gazelle lives in the hot deserts and barren wastes of Palestine and Syria as well as North Africa. Gazelles are distinguished from other antelope mainly by their small size and their large, lustrous eyes.
See *page 818*

[7-10A]

live apart except during the mating season. Six months after mating, the female produces one kid. Other kinds of tahr dwell in the hills of southern India and south-eastern Arabia.

DWELLER ON THE WINDSWEPT HEIGHTS

With its short horns and beardless chin, the Himalayan tahr is rather unlike most other wild goats. At home in inaccessible mountain regions, it is a difficult animal to find and shoot. The Indians prize the tahr for its bones, which they use to treat rheumatism.

MARKHORS—GOATS WITH PATRIARCHAL BEARDS

The Markhor, *Capra falconeri*, has long, shaggy hair, and in old males the beard extends from the chin down the underside of the throat. This wild goat follows along the margin between deep forest and higher snow-capped peaks where the tumbled rocks and steep cliffs are hidden by the last stand of woodland growth. It rarely comes out on open mountain slopes or bare crags above the timber line.

The domain of the markhor extends from Kashmir in India through Baluchistan to Afghanistan. There are five named forms, including the Astor Markhor and Punjab Markhor, that have long, spirally twisted horns. Famed as a hunter's trophy, they come out close together on top of the head and may curl in a wide, open spiral like a corkscrew

ITS HORNS MAKE A REMARKABLE TROPHY

The markhor is a handsome wild goat, greyish brown to white in colour and crowned with massive twisting horns. It has a long mane, and its beard almost reaches its knees. This superb animal, found from Kashmir to Afghanistan, is sometimes described as the "king of the wild goats"; the Persians named it markhor, which means "snake-eater".

or straight with two keels winding round and round like a screw. The Himalayan Markhor is the biggest of the wild goats—it may stand over forty inches high and weigh more than two hundred pounds.

FAMOUS BREEDS OF DOMESTIC SHEEP

There is a vast difference between wild sheep and the forty breeds of domestic sheep. The domestic sheep have a long tail and a woolly fleece, whereas the wild varieties have a short tail and a stiff, hairy coat. It was man's selective breeding that made the sheep the valuable wool-bearer it is today. Most authorities are agreed that the domestic sheep was derived from the Red Sheep, *Ovis orientalis*.

A FORTY-POUND TAIL

Sheep are the chief wealth of the pastoral tribes of Asia. In Turkistan the nomad Kirghiz live almost entirely on mutton. They have developed a variety of sheep known as the Dumba, which has an excess of fat on the buttocks. This breed possesses a long, fat tail that may weigh up to forty pounds. In Tashkent the author saw a prize-winning specimen that carried its huge tail in a little cart harnessed to the sheep. The Kirghiz not only eat the mutton but use the wool for clothing and beat it into heavy felt for covering their yurts, or tents.

MERINO AND PERSIAN LAMB

The Merino Sheep of Spain is famous for its wool; often it is so thick that it covers the animal's eyes. The Spaniards introduced the merino into America at an early date, and it has also found a good home in Australia. This hardy, sociable animal is said to produce more and finer wool than any other sheep. Its mutton, however, is not highly esteemed.

It is from the Caracul or Karacul that we get the Persian lamb or broadtail, originally referred to as Astrakhan. The best pelts are taken from caracul lambs when they are between a week and ten days old, for then the curl is at its best. Black pelts are the most desirable. These sturdy animals are at home in semi-arid regions—particularly in Bokhara, in the Uzbek republic of the Soviet Union.

A good deal of Australia's prosperity today is based on the raising of sheep. Western Asia and the western part of the United States are also responsible for much of the world's wool. Britain, too, is a noted breeder of sheep for wool and mutton; the Cheviot Sheep of Scotland, Southdown Sheep, and Shropshire Sheep are three noted British breeds.

SHEEP IN BIBLICAL TIMES

No other animal gets as much notice in the Bible as the sheep. This animal played an important part in the religious, civil, and domestic life of the ancient Hebrews. As for the nomadic Arabs, they are just as dependent on their sheep today as they were in Biblical times. They must still travel to suit the convenience of the animals; the

Arabs cannot stay in one locality longer than the pasturage will support the flocks.

WELLS IN THE DESERT

In ancient times sheep were tended more carefully than we think. The thought of obtaining water for his flock was uppermost in the shepherd's mind. Rarely, if at all, did sheep die of thirst—even when crossing large deserts which lacked surface water. The shepherd knew the hidden wells. His solicitous care has been immortalized in the forcible imagery of David, the shepherd poet: "The Lord is my shepherd; I shall not want. He maketh me to lie down in green pastures; He leadeth me beside the still waters."

The sheep were always watered at noon—never earlier or later in the day. The shepherd knew all his sheep by name and did not need to drive them. Sheep were kept more for their milk than their flesh. (Today our main product from the milk of these animals is Roquefort cheese, originally made in France.)

Sacred Trumpets. The horn of the ram had a special value for the ancient Hebrews; from it was made the sacred trumpet—the *shofar*. Mosaic law required these horns to be sounded on certain religious occasions. Each jubilee year was ushered in by the blasts of the sacred trumpets. The walls of Jericho fell, so the Scriptures tell us, when the trumpets of rams' horns were blown on the seventh day.

The Sacrificial Lamb. The sheep was important above all as a sacrifice. Mosaic law specified the age and sex of the sheep to be used. A young male lamb was the usual sacrifice.

The basic rite was the sacrifice of the Paschal lamb, the precursor of Christianity's Lamb of God, which taketh away the sins of the world. The lamb was killed for the feast of the Passover, and the blood was sprinkled with hyssop on the altar. Its flesh was eaten in haste; whatever was left, was consumed by fire.

A SPECTACULAR SHEEP

The Rocky Mountain Bighorn Sheep, *Ovis canadensis*, does not conform to our conventional notions about sheep. There are several kinds of bighorns, but this is the typical bighorn, the best known, the largest, and the one with the widest distribution.

Some authorities consider the Rocky Mountain bighorn America's finest game animal. At that, the bighorn would not have much to fear from the average sportsman if it were not for the telescopic sights and supercharged ammunition of the modern high-power rifle. The bighorn has extremely sharp eyesight and long-range vision. Its sense of smell is exceptionally acute. Its ears are attuned to catch the faintest sound.

HOW THE BIGHORN NEGOTIATES CRAGS AND CLIFFS

Though goats are excellent climbers, they by no means match the bounding swiftness of bighorn sheep. The feet of the bighorn are equipped with soft elastic pads that absorb the shocks of a bouncing gait and also provide an effective grip on hard, rough, or slippery surfaces.

Sailing Off into Space. There are few cliffs that bighorns cannot surmount—not carefully and step by step like a mountain goat, but at a seemingly heedless and breakneck gallop. Observers have watched these sheep careering down precipitous cliffs, leaping twenty feet at a time and breaking their speed by bouncing without hesitation from one narrow ledge of rock to another. Near the bottom of the cliff they sail off into the air with a final majestic bound, to alight on all four feet on the floor of the valley.

Occasionally a bighorn does crash to its death in one of these magnificent charges, but it is usually the ram and not the ewe that dies in this way.

Barring fatal accidents, and also the possibility of its being killed by wolves or bears, the bighorn can look forward to a long, happy life on the sunlit mountain tops. The average mountain sheep has passed its prime at ten or twelve years of age and is old at sixteen; under very favourable conditions, it may live to the grand old age of twenty years. But this is exceptional.

BATTERING RAMS

Francisco Coronado, the famous Spanish explorer of the American South-west, was the first white man to see the bighorn. He alluded to the animal in a letter, dated 3 August, 1540, to the governor of

Mexico, describing it as a sheep as big as a horse with large horns that were something to marvel at.

Actually, a full-grown bighorn may average forty inches in shoulder height.

Its weight may range between 175 and 350 pounds. The horns of mature rams often form more than one full turn, the record length being a trifle short of fifty inches. Ewes have smaller, compressed horns seldom exceeding fifteen inches in length.

The bighorn's summer coat is dark (or greyish) brown; its winter covering is lighter and greyer. The hair, like that of other wild sheep, is not woolly as in domestic sheep; instead, it is long, coarse, and full, like a deer's.

Mating Battles. Mountain sheep are herd animals, but the males and females do not mix except for a brief period in December during the mating season. At this time the rams vie fiercely with each other for possession of the ewes. They indulge in none of the pre-battle antics typical of moose or other horned beasts; they do not trumpet defiance at each other or roar challenging cries to combat. Instead, they settle down to serious fighting with little preliminary skirmishing.

Almost like professional boxers, two antagonists size up each other critically; then, after backing off a hundred feet or so, they charge headlong at about twenty miles per hour, crashing together in a smashing impact that can be heard two miles away on a still day. Again and again they repeat the battering onslaughts, until superior strength and endurance determine the ultimate victor.

GRANDMOTHER KNOWS BEST

By January the mating season is over, and the rams calmly resume their bachelor ways; even though they meet a flock of ewes, the males now pass them by indifferently, preferring the companionship of their own sex.

The lambs, usually two to each female, are born in late May or June. At first the mothers hide them and lick them; "owning" the lamb, as it is called, is a ritual never omitted. Before the day is out, the young are skipping about, following their mother, and are soon ready to join the herd.

The ewes and their yearling lambs associate in small flocks rarely numbering more than twenty head. The herd leader is a wise, portly ewe, the grandmother of much of the flock but still young enough to bear offspring annually. She keeps constant watch over her charges, since the safety of the entire group depends on her judgment and guidance.

AN ANIMAL WELL NAMED

The bighorn sheep, with its great, curling horns, is a creature easy to recognize. Although its coat is hairy rather than woolly, the animal is a true sheep all the same. Bighorns are silent as a rule, but occasionally they will emit a loud snort.

A DELICATE EATER

The bighorn is rather particular about its food and eats nothing but sweet, fresh mountain grasses and flowers; it rarely, if ever, browses on shrubs. All summer long the bighorn grazes in the upland meadows and grassy hillsides above the timber line. When the vegetation gets sparse and thin, the rams go a little higher to the edge of the rocky crags.

In the winter there is a general movement toward the shelter of the timber and the lower valleys. The bighorn, however, keeps to its own familiar territory or home range, where it knows all the trails and lush feeding grounds.

Some mountain sheep live in sun-baked sandy wastes, and they are thought to be able to get along without water; in fact, some authors go so far as to claim that these desert-loving sheep never drink. The chances are, though, that the sheep know of a secret waterhole to visit, though they may have to travel twenty miles to get a drink. They no doubt get considerable plant juices from the fat cactus leaves.

Aside from the typical bighorn, there are nine geographical varieties, including the Desert Bighorns and the Badlands Bighorn. They range from southern British Columbia to north-western Chihuahua, Mexico, and are also found in eastern Siberia.

RELATIVES OF THE BIGHORN

Fantastic Climbers. In northern British Columbia the author once came upon twenty-five big rams. They were Stone's Sheep, *Ovis dalli stonei*, and they were resting on a little hill surrounded by a huge natural amphitheatre. It seemed to the author that he had them cornered —unbroken walls of rock rose straight up two thousand feet on all sides, except for the entrance.

Unnoticed was a fold in the face of the cliff forming nothing more than an angle; up this the twenty-five rams went unhesitatingly in quick succession, bouncing back and forth like rubber balls. Higher and higher they went, and finally the last one was over the top. A pause of even a fraction of a second in that stupendous climb would have meant certain death on the ragged rocks below.

Stone's sheep, also known as the blue sheep or black sheep (it is deep grey to blackish brown in colour), dwells in British Columbia. It has a close relative in the White Sheep, or Dall's Sheep, *Ovis dalli dalli*.

Encounter in the Wild. With the exception of man, few enemies endanger the life of the white sheep, an animal that closely resembles the Rocky Mountain bighorn but for its white, or yellowish-white, colour.

Wolves and lynxes are swift enough to menace mature sheep, but only seldom do they succeed in making a meal of them.

On one occasion, Charles Sheldon, a noted observer of Alaskan game, noticed some sheep behaving strangely on the north side of the Alaska Range. He says: "I soon saw on the ground, at the foot of the slope, a sheep apparently dead, with a bloody head. Then immediately a lynx was looking at me. It quickly ran up the creek a short distance and disappeared in the rocks. Following rapidly, I saw it sitting on a ledge and shot it. Bringing it back to the sheep, I found that it had just pulled the sheep down the slope. I had missed seeing it by a minute only.

"The snow revealed part of the story. The lynx had waited on a rock about 500 feet up, and, as the ram (about two years old) crossed the slide, the lynx sprang on its back, and fastened its teeth in the left eye. Together they came down the slide, and at the bottom a struggle ensued. The lynx lost its hold and fastened again to the right eye. Not another tooth mark was on the sheep."

Though the white sheep is the smallest of American wild sheep (it stands a little over three feet at the shoulder), its record horn length is forty-seven and one-half inches.

This sheep dwells in the mountains of Alaska and in the north-western part of Canada.

THE LARGEST LIVING SHEEP

The Ammon, or Argali, *Ovis ammon*, the largest of all living wild sheep, lives on the highlands of central Asia, from Bokhara to Mongolia and Kamchatka. Here it is at home on grassy hillsides and meadows above the timber line. An agile mountain-climber, the argali can travel faster than any of the goats over precipitous crags and rugged mountain peaks.

The argali may attain a shoulder height of four feet and a weight of 350 pounds.

The horns of the rams are large and massive; they curl outward from the side of the head and frequently make more than one complete turn.

A FIND OF MARCO POLO'S

In the thirteenth century, the famous Venetian traveller Marco Polo first discovered the magnificent Pamir Argali, also known as Marco Polo's Sheep. However, this animal remained practically unknown to western science until specimens were obtained for the British Museum in 1874. The comparatively slender but still massive horns of Marco Polo's sheep curve sharply away from the head, forming more than one complete turn that may measure seventy-five inches along the outside edge.

ABOVE THE CLOUDS

Marco Polo's sheep is reported as living in herds, often of considerable size, on the Pamir plateau of southern central Asia. These herds resort to the most inaccessible and difficult mountain ranges at elevations of ten to twelve thousand feet, where the age-worn shale slides and there is a total absence of cover. After days of hard going in the rarefied air of this remote and secluded retreat, which is without trails and remains unmapped to this day, one may have the satisfaction of viewing the "heraldic beast of central Asia".

At first one sees nothing but the great curling horns, but they are attached to a giant ram that has found himself an impregnable position on top of some isolated grassy knoll. Though he may be a battle-scarred old warrior retired to a lonely but peaceful existence away from the herd, and may even be drowsing in the sunshine, he will quickly leap out of sight at the first sign of danger.

After that he will not pause until he has passed on to the next mountain range.

There are twelve geographical races of Argali, including the Littledale Sheep of the Tien Shan.

OTHER INTERESTING WILD SHEEP

The Himalayan Bharal, or Blue Sheep, *Pseudois nayaur,* while definitely not a goat, has the markings and horns of one, though it lacks the strong, disagreeable odour of the typical goat. The blue sheep dwells among the heights of the mountain ranges of central Asia from Tibet to western China. In summer it may be found at elevations of seventeen thousand feet, and even in winter it probably never descends below ten thousand feet.

Blue sheep gather in flocks of eight to more than fifty. Watchful and wary animals, they take, or at least seem to take, the precaution of stationing a sentry on a high point amid the jagged rocks, while the rest of the herd feeds on grassy slopes high above the timber line. The sentinel remains motionless, almost invisible in its surroundings, until some suspicious occurrence sends it bounding from its post. The herd immediately races to refuge among steep crags, which they prefer to seeking shelter in the neighbouring bush.

The sexes always live separately except during the breeding season. After mating, the rams leave the ewes in June or July. The lambs are born one hundred and sixty days later. Twins are not uncommon, and the young are not weaned until fully three-quarters grown. There are two local races, the Chinese Bharal and the Kansu Bharal.

FAMED BLUE SHEEP OF THE HIMALAYAS

The bharal, with its down-curving horns, is one of the common wild sheep of the mountains of central Asia. In its lofty homeland it is a most difficult animal to hunt, but its mutton is said to be excellent. The bharal is easy to domesticate. Sheep, in general, are less capricious and adventuresome than goats.

The Aoudad, or Barbary Sheep, *Ammotragus lervia,* is also known as the Udad, Audad, Arui, Fechstal, and Maned Sheep. It is the only wild sheep found in Africa and may be recognized by its uniform tawny colour and the fringe of long hair hanging from its throat, chest, and the upper parts of its forelegs. It has a longer tail than other wild sheep. There are seven varieties of aoudad. The animal stands over three feet at the shoulder, and its horns may be thirty inches long.

This big sheep lives in small family groups, except for the rams, which are more or less solitary except for the breeding season. The animal is at home in the Atlas Mountains and the Aures that fringe the Sahara

Desert. It often is seen on isolated outcrops of rock that jut out of the burning desert and even on arid, level ground almost destitute of vegetation and water.

THE BIG BARBARY SHEEP

A stately-looking creature indeed is the ram pictured above—the aoudad, or Barbary sheep. Standing amidst the rocky crags of the North African mountains, where it lives, often the animal can hardly be seen, unless it chances to be silhouetted against the sky.

The Mouflon, *Ovis musimon*, is one of the very few wild sheep in Europe. It is a native of the mountains of Sardinia and Corsica, but has been introduced into Hungary, Austria, Czechoslovakia, and other countries. It is a rather small species, reddish brown in colour with a whitish saddle in winter. The ewes usually, but not always, have horns.

The Red Sheep, or Gmelin's Sheep, *Ovis orientalis*, is yellow or fox-red in summer and brownish in winter, with a grey saddle patch. The horns are not unlike those of the mouflon, but usually curve more sharply backward and terminate behind the head. There are several species of red sheep that inhabit the arid rocky mountain ridges of Asia Minor, Transcaucasia, Persia and Cyprus.

The Urial, Gad or Shapo, *Ovis vignei*, is also known as the Oorial or Sha. It has an extensive range and is spread over the mountains of north-west India through Afghanistan to Transcaspia, Turkestan, and Russia. This is a variously coloured sheep but usually it is reddish brown. The males have long, slender horns that form a large, open curl.

While it is generally conceded that most of our domestic sheep were derived from the red sheep, the mouflon and the urial cannot be entirely excluded as possible ancestors.

Evolution and the Story of Animal Life

SCIENTISTS tell us that our earth came into being some three billion years ago. The infant planet, when it became separated from its mother, the sun, was a mass of blazing gas, much as the sun is today. In time—and it was a very long time—this gas cooled and turned solid. Rocks began to form.

Some of our rocks are now calculated to be nearly two billion years old. It is possible that life on earth extends almost back to the age of these rocks! These figures, it is true, are staggering, but they are finite and something that we can understand.

How did life begin? That is a question that has fascinated man ever since he became a thinking creature. In our own days, we have found a reasonable answer, and doubtless we shall be able to prove its accuracy before long.

It appears that sometime during the first two billion years or so of our planet's history the spark of life was born. A combination of materials and conditions came together and spontaneously produced this novel element on earth. It probably began as the result of the wearing down and rotting of minerals and rocks, which released certain chemical elements; the radiant energy provided by the rays of sunlight may well have played a part.

LIFE BEGINS IN THE WATER

The birthplace of life, most scientists are convinced, was in the water. Even today all living things must have water in some form to survive. No creature can breathe air or digest its food without water. Where species of animal life have been traced back to primitive types, the trail always leads to the water. The oldest known fossils, dating back five hundred million years, are of marine origin.

Where air, water, and land come together, there is and always has been a theatre of great activity. It was in the land waters or inland seas, rather than the primitive oceans, that life must have started. It had its beginning, we believe, where the tides flowed and receded over warm mud and ooze or steaming beaches of hot sand.

When our planet was young, the atmosphere was heavy with moisture, and warm rain almost incessantly poured down on the hot earth. The sun blazed on an unshaded land and set in a quarter of the time it takes today. Particles of organic compounds were formed in this setting, and they took on a living individuality. They fed and grew, and were capable of motion. It was these strange new things on earth that started the endless chain of dying and being born again.

Of these earliest forms of life we know little or nothing. They must have been simple, one-celled, virus-like molecules, so minute in size that they could not be seen through our most powerful microscope. These molecules were more vegetable than animal, but they came before either.

LIFE FROM NOT-LIFE

How could life come from not-life, you may wonder. Is all this a romantic conception? Such hardly seems to be the case. The basic substances that make up our earth are the same substances we find within our bodies.

Eminent scientists like Dr. Harold C. Urey, the great American physicist who won the Nobel Prize, have theorized that life came into being when methane (marsh gas), hydrogen, and certain other factors met. One of Dr. Urey's students has supplied good support for this hypothesis. The scientific world was recently startled to learn that this man had brought these constituents together under appropriate conditions in a laboratory and produced amino-acids, which are the building-blocks of all living matter. We may not be so far away from creating living tissue itself.

THE FIRST LIVING THINGS

For the first live molecule to develop into a tiny, one-celled animal the size of the amoeba, which is visible under the microscope, untold aeons of time were required. The span of years was considerably greater than that taken for the first one-celled animal to evolve into an elephant or a man.

More than three-quarters of the earth's history had already passed before the one-celled jelly-like plant-animals, the Protozoa, the earliest *known* forms of life, appeared. They were much the same as living forms of today. Some had supporting body structures; often they were very beautiful. Contemporary with the early forms of animal life was the archaic vegetable matter, later the lower vegetation, and on to the higher plants.

As vegetation progressed, so the animal life evolved. One depended on the other; at least animal life was dependent on vegetation for its starches and proteins, as it still is today.

The very simplest forms of life left no records. It was not until living things had acquired a supporting structure like a skeleton or a shell that vestiges of their existence could be preserved or fossilized in tablets of rock. All the pages of the earth's rock diary have not yet been opened, but in the ones already available we may read the rough outlines of the story of how simple one-celled microscopic forms of primitive life developed into the highly specialized animals of the present day.

OUT OF THE WATER AND ON TO DRY LAND

At first life had to keep close to the shallow shore water. It was dependent on air dissolved in water, and sunlight. It faced the constant danger of being stranded.

One essential characteristic of life is changeability. Living matter is unstable, and these first living things changed in many ways and branched out in many directions. After a while there were water animals with backbones. Where there had been only invertebrates to begin with, now vertebrates also existed. The fishes came into being.

So now we have fairly well-developed animals in the water, but none on land.

Before living creatures could leave the water with impunity, they had to acquire a suitable breathing apparatus. A fish, taken out of the water, does not immediately die from lack of water but because its gills dry up and it cannot breathe. This was the problem, and before it could be solved some of the water animals had to change still further. In time they did. They developed lungs of a sort, and circumstances obliged the animals to use them out of water.

The fishes, as such, stayed in the water. But from their stock there had developed some whose large, strong fins could serve as legs. These animals were either stranded or else they crawled from the mud on to dry land. They became primitive amphibians—animals that may live on land but generally deposit their eggs in water, as their finny forefathers did. The ancient amphibians became the ancestors of the reptiles, birds, and mammals of yesterday and today.

The life cycle of the frog, an amphibian, shows the principle of liberation from the water—but incomplete liberation. The female lays her eggs in the water. From these, in a short while, tadpoles develop. The tadpole has gills to breathe air dissolved in the water, and feeds on minute vegetable matter.

Early in life, the tadpole is little more than a head and a tail. But later the tadpole grows hind legs and then fore legs and then lungs— the equipment of a land animal—and loses its tail and gills. The creature is now a frog, and can leave the water to live in the air and feed on animal matter.

When it wants to breed, however, it must return to the water to lay its eggs, for they need moisture in order to develop.

THE INSECTS GO THEIR OWN WAY

The insects and their close relatives had a parallel development. Insects came of a stock derived from primitive forms (the trilobite is an example) that lived in the land waters and became amphibious.

[7-11]

Like the weasel cats, the Rocky Mountain goat belongs to a separate family with a double name—goat antelope—because, being neither, it possesses characteristics of both. Very much at home on the broken crags and treacherous mountain ledges far above the timber line, the thick-haired mountain goat has only one real enemy—Nature itself. *See page 824*

With the possible exception of man and his high-powered rifle with telescopic sights, mountain sheep fear little if anything. Galloping with utter abandon, apparently, where the goat antelope and true goats carefully pick their way, one will occasionally miss its footing—with disastrous results. *See page 846*

[7-11A]

The ibex is the common wild goat of the Old World and exists in many varieties, one of which is believed to be the stock from which our domestic goats were derived. Agile and sure-footed, possessed of acute powers of sight, hearing and smell—all of the ibex's senses seem to be sharpened by the cold clear air of the lofty pinnacles it calls home.

See page 840

[7-12]

[7-12A]

The turs of Asia also prefer to live on lofty precipices above the snow line. While some varieties of this species are true goats, some are not quite goats yet not quite sheep either, so the tur forms a connecting link between the two.   See page 842

Animals are frequently named after their discoverers: *Ovis dalli dalli* is Dall's sheep, and closely resembles the Rocky Mountain bighorn except for its white, or near-white, colour. Against the sky they make an interesting picture, bouncing along like rubber balls over apparently impassable terrain. *See page 850*

[7-13]

[7-13A]

Standing a little over three feet at the shoulder, the Dall (or white sheep) is the smallest of American wild sheep, but its record horn length is just under four feet. It dwells in the mountains of Alaska and the northwestern part of Canada. *See page 850*

[7-13B]

Africa's only wild sheep, the aoudad or Barbary sheep, makes its home on isolated outcrops of rock in the burning desert, or on the barren, arid level ground in the surrounding area. Its distinguishing mark is the long fringe of hair growing from its throat, chest and upper forelegs. *See page 853*

See Evolution and the Story of Animal Life. Page 855

Pteranodon lived in the Cretaceous period 90 million years ago. Largest of the group of flying reptiles, its wing span measured from 15 to 27 feet. (Credit for pictures and text on this and the following two pages is given to J. W. Thompson, Scientific Supplies Company.)

[7-14A]

The Dimetrodon of Upper Permian times—190 million years ago—is best known from fossils found in northern Texas. It was about 11 feet long with half of the length in tail; there is no satisfactory explanation for the 3-foot sail that projected from the back.

[7-14B]

Diplodocus, the longest dinosaur known, measured up to 88 feet. This monster lived in the Upper Jurassic period, 125 million years ago.

[7-14C]

Also in the Cretaceous period but 100 million years ago, a 6 to 8 foot dinosaur, Protoceratops, lived in China. Scientists have found fossilized, just ready to hatch, eggs of this animal, proving that dinosaurs as a whole were reptiles.

In the earliest stages they were wingless—much like the "silverfish" we find in bathrooms today. The first insects of which we have a record show up with well-developed wings in deposits laid down in the early Carboniferous period, three hundred million years ago. Insects were capable of flight fifty million years before the reptiles and the birds.

The size of the ancient insects was truly amazing; at no other time in the history of the earth have they grown so large. There were carnivorous dragonflies that had a wing-spread of twenty-nine inches. Many of the insects of today reflect their amphibious origin; like our frogs, they spend the early part of their lives in the water.

EVOLUTION AND THE STRUGGLE FOR SURVIVAL

A million kinds of animals exist in the world today (three-quarters of this number are insects). Of the many millions of creatures in each species no two are exactly alike—in fact, no two organisms or parts of an organism are precisely alike—no matter how closely related. Some species of fish, the ling for example, may produce twenty-eight million eggs at a time—but no two of the progeny are exactly the same. Some forms of life multiply at the rate of six hundred generations in a year.

The essential factor behind evolution is the teeming abundance of life from which to draw. In general, reproduction of life is far in excess of the numbers that can possibly survive. Each animal has to face keen competition—it has a host of rivals for the existing food supply. Of the many millions of animals born each year, only a relative few live to reach maturity and the breeding stage.

Those that survive in the long run do so because they were born with some slight difference—some advantage over their fellow beings. This is the starting point of what is called "natural selection" or "survival of the fittest", a concept identified with the names of Charles Darwin.

ONLY THE FIT SHALL LIVE

What sort of advantages make a creature better fitted than its fellows to cope with the conditions of existence? The variation in the animal may be fractional, perhaps only just a shade in colour that blends more perfectly with its surroundings than do the hues of the rest of its kind. It is just that small advantage that permits one animal to survive while the others must perish. Or the survivor may be bigger or faster. It may have a longer neck and longer legs, and be able to get at food which is higher up on a tree—food that its brothers and sisters cannot reach.

Each animal puts to the best use its own advantages and abilities in its efforts to survive. Within a given species, this might appear to be competitive rivalry. But it is hardly a vicious contest in the human sense. There is no malicious intent to harm; no hatred or enmity is involved. There is no plotting or wilful exercise of cruelty, nor is there any love or sympathy meted out among the competitors.

Whatever an animal's inborn advantage is, it may on occasion be handed on to succeeding generations. The same thing happens to inborn disadvantages. If the disadvantages are great, however, the animal will not live long enough to breed.

Creatures with genuine strong points will continue to multiply, and the strong points will be emphasized in their descendants, as one better-equipped animal mates with another one like it. The longer neck, for example, becomes longer—so, too, do the legs—and we have the giraffe, which is a far cry from the short-legged, short-necked ancestral stock that begot it.

Take horses as another instance. The first horses on earth were very small creatures with four toes. They were not fast enough to escape the enemies that developed in time, nor big and strong enough to fight them. Larger horses, ultimately with one toe (the hoof) evolved, and were equipped for a successful existence. These are the horses we know today. The others became extinct ages ago.

THE MEANING OF RADIATION

All that has been written here is a simplification of what happened in the history of life. That history, in the main, is a process of radiation, and an enormously complicated one at that.

Radiation, if it is not already clear, may be easily explained. To begin with, we find a single kind of animal—we call this a species. Some of its descendants vary from it, and in a number of instances these variations become permanent (at least for a long while). The original stock goes on, if it is well adapted to its circumstances, and so do the descendants. But they look less and less alike, and they cannot interbreed, as the generations mount up. (They have become different species.)

A later generation may change again, and become still more different from its ancestral type. This may go on *ad infinitum*. Some lines become extinct in time. Or the original stock, from which the first variations sprang, may produce still different forms after a long or short while.

The transformations of the species may be very great indeed. Not just new species are produced—entirely new classes of life may evolve. The sparrow on your lawn is a descendant of gliding and flying reptiles of perhaps a hundred million years ago—it is actually a cousin of the dinosaurs! Man himself is the latest offspring of small shrew-like mammals that cowered in the grass as the dinosaurs lumbered by and the first leathery-winged birds circled overhead. But a long line of gradually changing tree-dwellers—finally a race of large-bodied apelike creatures—had to evolve before the first man could spring from their loins.

AN ANIMAL'S SURROUNDINGS

Survival, in the final analysis, is always survival within a certain environment. The climate in a given region is never stable, but may change in the course of time from warm to cold or from dry to wet. The creature that through natural selection (the survival of the fittest) becomes adapted to conditions of intense cold may not survive a change to a warm climate. At one time, parts of the earth were covered with snow and ice. It happened that certain species developed long hairy coats, and were equipped to withstand the cold. These were such animals as the woolly mammoth and woolly rhinoceros. When the ice receded and disappeared, so did these woolly giants. Their relatives, the elephants and rhinoceroses pure and simple, have fared better.

There were many more species in past geological time than there are alive in the world today. Just think, for a moment, of the Age of Reptiles. The dinosaurs—"glorified reptiles" they have been called —existed in huge numbers and great variety long ages ago. They dominated the earth for millions of years when the climate was warm and moist. As times changed, the rich swamps and greenland in which the dinosaurs had luxuriated ceased to exist; the dinosaurs were finished. But minute shrewlike mammals, descended from the same reptile ancestors as the dinosaurs, did not have to fear the change. On the contrary, it did them good by removing their big competitors. Thus the Age of Mammals could begin.

THE DANGER OF BECOMING TOO SPECIALIZED

We have seen that animals are variable. Before birth, random changes occur in them, either slow or fast, and they become new kinds of animals. The variation in a species may enable it to meet the requirements for survival in an environment. But often, when an animal becomes very specialized—like the woolly mammoth or the dinosaur—marked changes in its environment may mean its doom. Some of the dinosaurs' contemporaries—the birds are an example—managed to go on because they were adapted to meet the new circumstances.

There are many animals that have changed little or not at all from the parent form through countless generations. (Oysters of today appear to be very similar to oysters that lived two hundred million years ago.)

This does not imply, however, that evolution has stopped in a particular form—that the creature has reached a state of "perfection". It might indicate that such an animal has acquired the features or qualities necessary to survive, and has successfully met the competition. If conditions changed, a new form or variation might be favoured by them, and take the place of the old.

THE IMPORTANCE OF HEREDITY

Heredity is the channel through which the various forms of life are handed on. It is a conservative factor that enables a new form to proceed to its ultimate goal and to persist. In general, the variation of an individual must be handed down through generations before it can be properly developed and put to use. The horses passed through many stages before they reached the efficient form of the modern species.

Just how variations become inheritable is one of the mysteries of evolution.

Changes arising from habits or accidents cannot be inherited. Scientists have tried cutting off the tail of mice through numerous generations, yet never have they succeeded in reducing the length of the tail in the last born.

The change in a species comes with variations that occur in the chromosomes, the heredity-bearers within the animal. Although the chromosomes are usually fixed in number for each species, they are somewhat variable in the traits they embody; it is these variations that, when favoured by natural conditions, enable a species to change and survive.

Not all of the changes within a species are outward, or physical. A creature's impulses may evolve and be passed on by heredity. Birds migrate by inherited impulse; insects are directed to certain flowers by it; a bee dances to tell its fellows where there is nectar to be found, and it knows how to perform this dance without ever having seen another bee.

Sociability is handed on by animals as a survival trait. Some animals can exist only if they live together in large colonies or flocks. When the huge flocks of passenger pigeons were reduced by human intervention to a few stragglers, they became extinct; the few left automatically disappeared, leaving no offspring.

DARWIN'S CONTRIBUTION

Relatively speaking, all of this is new knowledge. The theory of evolution is hardly one hundred years old, and, as is widely known, we trace it back to Charles Darwin, the great English biologist. Only in the light of Darwin's theory, first set forth in his book *The Origin of Species* (1859), can we understand the principle of radiation—why there are hundreds of species of rats, thousands of species of beetles, all alike and yet different. When Darwin appeared upon the scene, it was almost universally believed that species were immutable—that each one had been as it was since the beginning of time.

It is to Darwin's immortal credit that he was able to perceive what has since become so obvious. Through evolution he explained how amphibians developed into reptiles; how reptiles changed in one direction to become birds, and in another to become mammals. Recent investigators have discarded some of the details of Darwin's thought, but in its main outlines it is the only explanation accepted by the majority of scientists as to how all the forms of life, both animal and vegetable, came into being.

ANIMALS OLD AND NEW

To appreciate fully the highly specialized mammals of this modern age, we must consider the wonderful story of how they developed. That story, as already suggested, takes us back to the dim ages of prehistory.

The earliest of the great geological eras of our earth was the Archeozoic ("primitive life"), which is estimated to have started approximately two billion years ago. The earth, then, was perhaps already a billion years old. In the Archeozoic era life is believed to have had its first beginnings. We have found fossil carbon in the rocks that were laid down at that time, indicating that some form of life existed—probably the very simple one-celled types of plants and animals discussed earlier.

During the second great era, the Proterozoic ("former life"), more complex living things developed from the simpler ones that had preceded them. Bacteria, seaweeds, sponges, and various other kinds of animals without backbones made their appearance and established themselves.

In the earliest period of the Paleozoic era ("ancient life"), the next major division of time, the shelled invertebrates were the dominant form of animal life, seaweeds the dominant plant life. Fishes, the first animals with backbones, appeared later. These were followed by the amphibians and the primitive reptiles. Ferns, horsetails, and related plants developed in great stretches of forests and swamps. (On the accompanying Geological Timetable of Animal Life you will see typical animals of the Permian, Upper Carboniferous, Devonian, and other periods—spans of time which take their name from ancient rock strata.)

The Mesozoic ("middle life") was the Age of Reptiles. These animals completely dominated the waters of the earth, the lands, and the air.

Dinosaurs and flying dragons abounded, while the birds and mammals made their first precarious beginnings, as did the true flowering plants.

THE AGE OF MAMMALS

It was not until a hundred million years later, in the Cenozoic ("recent life"), the fifth great era of geological time, that the mammals rose above the ranks of the reptiles and amphibians to become the major power in the world. The Age of Mammals extends through to the present day. Opening more than sixty million years ago, it was divided into periods of great progress and long periods of transition when many of the common mammals disappeared and new forms developed.

Thousands, perhaps millions, of years elapsed between the close of one period and the rise of another. Even so, at these times there were many "holdover" species from the earlier animal life that continued on with the new. In some parts of the world the intermission between the periods appears to be marked by an abrupt beginning and ending, but elsewhere there was a continuity of progressive development of the mammals from the older periods to the new.

Time and again, the older and more primitive forms were replaced by new and more modern species, which for thousands of years flourished, multiplied, and enriched the earth. Then gradually a new fauna would arise. These major transitions were brought about by the evolution of the earth itself, the change in climatic conditions, and in part by restriction of habitat caused by the encroachment and recession of the seas.

The first major period in the Age of Mammals was the Eocene ("dawn of the new"), which lasted about thirty or thirty-five million years. At the beginning of this period (the first part is sometimes referred to as the Paleocene or "ancient new" period) the earth was populated with many strange primitive mammals: they were thickset, heavily built creatures with short legs. Toward the end of the Eocene there was considerable improvement. Many rhinoceros-like animals appeared, and along with them the four-toed horses.

The Oligocene ("a little new") lasted about ten million years and represented a great advance over the Eocene. It was an age of giants. There were many kinds of rhinoceroses, such as North America's great Titanotheres, *Baluchitherium*, which was fourteen feet high at the shoulder; giant pigs, three-toed horses, primitive flesh-eaters, and many other strange creatures abounded.

The next period, the Miocene ("less new"), lasted about ten million years and brought giraffe-like camels, deer, mastodons, and many horses. The plains and prairies were well stocked with big game and the forests were thickly populated.

The Pliocene ("more new") covered a period of about ten to twelve

TIMETABLE OF ANIMAL LIFE

ERA: CENOZOIC (61,000,000 YEARS)

PERIOD: RECENT (50,000 YEARS)
CHARACTERISTIC ANIMAL LIFE (MAMMALS)

| Chimpanzee | Gemsbok | Kangaroo |

PERIOD: PLEISTOCENE (1,000,000 YEARS)
CHARACTERISTIC ANIMAL LIFE (MAMMALS)

| Mammoth | Sabre-toothed Tiger | Giant Sloth |

PERIOD: PLIOCENE (10,000,000 YEARS)
CHARACTERISTIC ANIMAL LIFE (MAMMALS)

| Glyptodon | Pliocene Mastodon | Horned Gopher |

Note: The animals named and depicted in this chart represent merely a few forms that are characteristic of the various geological periods. It is not to be inferred that they are the only species in existence during a particular time.

TIMETABLE OF ANIMAL LIFE

ERA: CENOZOIC (61,000,000 YEARS)—*continued*

PERIOD: MIOCENE (10,000,000 YEARS)
CHARACTERISTIC ANIMAL LIFE (MAMMALS)

Giraffe Camel   Long-jawed Mastodon   Syndyoceras

PERIOD: OLIGOCENE (10,000,000 YEARS)
CHARACTERISTIC ANIMAL LIFE (MAMMALS)

Titanothere   Giant Pig   Creodon

PERIOD: EOCENE (20,000,000 YEARS)
CHARACTERISTIC ANIMAL LIFE (MAMMALS)

Uintatherium   Patriofelis   Four-toed Horse

TIMETABLE OF ANIMAL LIFE

ERA: CENOZOIC (61,000,000 YEARS)—*continued*

    PERIOD: PALEOCENE (10,000,000 YEARS)
    CHARACTERISTIC ANIMAL LIFE (MAMMALS)

Phenacodus   Ectoganus   Pantolambda

ERA: MESOZOIC (140,000,000 YEARS)

    PERIOD: CRETACEOUS (60,000,000 YEARS)
    CHARACTERISTIC ANIMAL LIFE (MAMMALS)

Mesozoic Mammal

    PERIOD: CRETACEOUS (60,000,000 YEARS)—*continued*
    CHARACTERISTIC ANIMAL LIFE (DINOSAURS)

Tyrannosaurus   Triceratops   Pteranodon

TIMETABLE OF ANIMAL LIFE

ERA: MESOZOIC (140,000,000 YEARS)—*continued*

PERIOD: JURASSIC (35,000,000 YEARS)
CHARACTERISTIC ANIMAL LIFE (DINOSAURS)

Stegosaurus

Archaeopteryx

Ichthyosaur

PERIOD: TRIASSIC (45,000,000 YEARS)
CHARACTERISTIC ANIMAL LIFE (DINOSAURS)

Placodus

Nothasaurus

Dicynodon

ERA: PALEOZOIC (340,000,000 YEARS)

PERIOD: PERMIAN (25,000,000 YEARS)
CHARACTERISTIC ANIMAL LIFE (PRIMITIVE REPTILES)

Pariasaur

Dimetrodon

Varanosaurus

TIMETABLE OF ANIMAL LIFE

ERA: PALEOZOIC (340,000,000 YEARS)—*continued*

PERIOD: UPPER CARBONIFEROUS (20,000,000 YEARS)
CHARACTERISTIC ANIMAL LIFE (AMPHIBIANS)

Diplovertebron   Diplocaulus

PERIOD: LOWER CARBONIFEROUS (30,000,000 YEARS)
CHARACTERISTIC ANIMAL LIFE (AMPHIBIANS)

Ichthyostege

PERIOD: DEVONIAN (65,000,000 YEARS)
CHARACTERISTIC ANIMAL LIFE (FISHES)

Lobe-finned Fish   Spine-bearing Shark

PERIOD: SILURIAN (35,000,000 YEARS)
CHARACTERISTIC ANIMAL LIFE (FISHES)

Armoured Fish   Jointed-neck Fish

TIMETABLE OF ANIMAL LIFE

ERA: PALEOZOIC (340,000,000 YEARS)—*continued*

PERIOD: ORDOVICIAN (75,000,000 YEARS)
CHARACTERISTIC ANIMAL LIFE (INVERTEBRATES)

Cephalopod

Stalked Crinoid

PERIOD: CAMBRIAN (90,000,000 YEARS)
CHARACTERISTIC ANIMAL LIFE (INVERTEBRATES)

Trilobite

Brachiopod

ERA: PROTEROZOIC—ARCHEOZOIC (1,500,000,000 YEARS)
CHARACTERISTIC ANIMAL LIFE (PRIMITIVE INVERTEBRATES)

Proterozoic Worms (three are shown)

Few fossils have been found that tell us of the earliest stages of life. For long ages, the single-celled animals, or protozoans, were a common form. Untold ages before them life had its beginnings in living molecules, but of these nothing remains.

million years and is noteworthy because animals like those we know today began to appear more and more. There were one-toed horses, rhinoceroses, elephants, lions, sabre-toothed tigers, deer, and antelope. The entire world was teeming with game of all kinds.

Dry periods came at the close of this wonderful era. In some places the plains and prairies were drained of moisture by the burning heat; the life-giving rivers and lakes dried up and were not replenished. In certain areas these dry periods increased in severity. The hot winds licked up the moisture on the land and the animals died by the thousands.

We find great masses of bones fossilized around what were once dried-up waterholes.

FINEST WILD LIFE EVER KNOWN

The Pleistocene ("most new") covered a period of about one million years, which brings us up to the mammals of the present day. They suffered great setbacks when a drastic climatic upheaval brought intense cold.

Waters of the oceans were transformed into snow on the polar ice caps, and the great glaciers moved south, destroying almost two-thirds of the wild life in northern regions. Four times the glaciers covered a good part of the earth.

The Pleistocene, up to the time of the Ice Age, brought the finest wild life this world has ever known. North America, as well as Asia, teemed with troops of horses, elephants, mastodons, llamas, camels, lions, tigers, yaks, in addition to all the types of animals alive today. The mastodons, woolly mammoths, sabre-toothed tigers, giant bison, and many other now extinct species survived the Ice Age, which itself lasted into the Recent period, and were alive on the earth up to fifteen thousand years ago. So far as we know, New World mammoths and ground sloths were contemporaries of the Indians, who came to the Americas perhaps twenty-five thousand years ago.

OF MAMMALS AND CONTINENTS

The shore lines of the large land-masses have changed comparatively little during the past sixty million years. During all this time there has been more or less free access between all the continents except Australia. At times, of course, South America was separated from

North America, even as North America is now cut off from Asia, but in the past there were land-bridges between them.

It is on the basis of this comparative freedom of access that we explain the fact that many "typical" North American animals—sheep, bison, deer, and bears are some—are actually of Asiatic origin; and others, such as horses and camels, which are found in Asia, but were not present in America in recent times, originated in the New World. This also explains why there are almost identical animals like the moose, mountain sheep, bear, and wolf in both North America and Asia. In general, living things have a tendency to spread out over as wide an area as possible, and this has helped keep these large land-masses well stocked with game.

However, today each large land-mass has its typical animals, no matter where they came from at the start. Africa has the most, for they sought out this warm haven when the Ice Age froze or chilled their former homelands. This continent is outstanding for its large number of antelopes, zebras, big-eared elephants, lions, buffaloes, hippopotamuses, rhinoceroses, gorillas, chimpanzees, and monkeys without grasping tails. Asia, with only a few antelopes and a large number of deer, is noted for its tigers, bears, goats, and ibex, mountain sheep, buffaloes, small-eared elephants, rhinoceroses, wild horses, and camels, as well as gibbons and many kinds of monkeys.

Europe once supported numerous wild oxen, deer, chamois, bison, and wild boars, but most of these have virtually vanished.

North America has its special forms of big game in the musk ox, mountain goat, and pronghorn; but it also is a country of deer, mountain sheep, cougars, and bears (formerly bison, too).

South America has its own particular group of animals, that includes the llamas, peccaries, tapirs, anteaters, sloths, armadillos, opossums, jaguars, capybaras, and a specialized group of monkeys, those with grasping tails.

The Australian region's outstanding animals are the marsupials—kangaroos, wallabies, koalas, and opossums—as well as the egg-layers, the platypuses and echidnas. New Zealand does not have a single native land mammal and never had any except two kinds of bats. All others found there today came in rather late or were imported.

Madagascar features a large variety of lemurs and a distinctly different group of insect-eating animals.

The seals are more or less concentrated about the polar regions, the sea lions and fur seals are found mostly in the Pacific Ocean and the southern seas; the sea cows are now restricted to the coastal waters of the warm seas. We find whales and porpoises on all seas, but they are most abundant in temperate and colder waters.

This, so to speak, is the mammal map of the world. It is a map that has not changed much during the brief span of time in which man has achieved dominion over other living things. In earlier ages it changed greatly. That the process of alteration has not been completed we may rest assured, as coastlines sink and mountains rise, and the climate gradually changes. Mother Earth never ceases in her activity, and what new wonders she may bring forth in the long tomorrow no mere member of one of her newer species can say.

[7-15]

See Evolution and the Story of Animal Life.   Page 855

The Woolly Rhinoceros was a dominant animal during the ice age in Europe. Remains found in caves indicate it was from 14 to 16 feet long, and the species is believed to have existed for six million years.

[7-15A]

This Mastodon lived in North America after the retreat of the last ice sheet, 15,000 to possibly 8,000 years ago.

[7-15B]

Entire bodies of the Woolly Mammoth have been found in Siberia and Alaska. Like the Woolly Rhinoceros it lived during the ice ages, although over a much shorter period of time.

[7-15C]

The giant or Irish Elk lived from late Pleistocene times until only a few thousand years ago. Its 10-foot antler spread destroyed it as eventually it could not negotiate the heavy forest growth that followed the last glaciation.

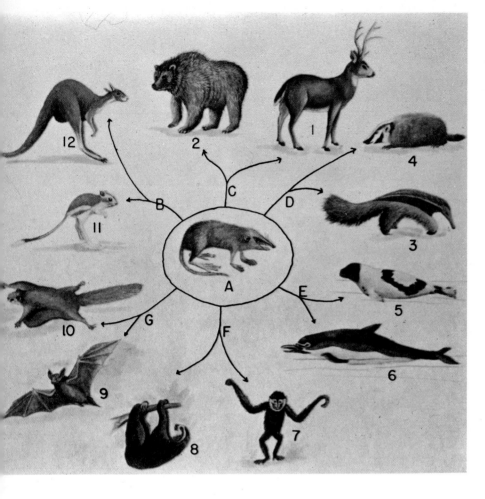

Divergence, or adaptive radiation, has occurred when animals
have arisen from (A) an ancestral
insectivore, and become divergent in methods of locomotion,
(B) leaping, as (11) jerboa and
(12) kangaroo; (C) walking and
running, as (1) deer and (2) bear;
(D) digging, as (3) giant ant-eater
and (4) badger; (E) swimming, as
(5) seal and (6) dolphin; (F) hanging and climbing, as (7) gibbon
and (8) sloth; (G) flying and gliding, as (9) bat and (10) flying
squirrel.

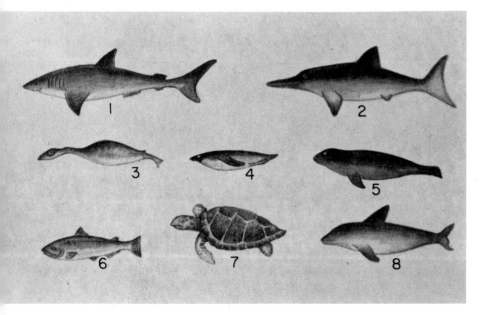

Adaptive convergence has occurred when animals of different
groups have come to live in a
common environment, as these
examples have become stream-
lined for easy movement in water:
(1) shark, (2) Ichthyosaur (an ancient sea monster), (3) hesperor-
nis (an ancient toothed bird), (4)
penguin, (5) seal, (6) salmon, (7)
turtle, and (8) dolphin.

Snakes, Turtles and Lizards

THE chances are that snakes either fascinate you or arouse your intense dislike. Few people are neutral, and children are quick to adopt their parents' admiration or profound distaste for the slithering reptiles. However, some children are so fond of snakes that they will bring them home for pets regardless of how their families receive the creatures. Under such circumstances one conscientious mother said to me:

"*How* can I make myself like snakes? They revolt me, but my boys are always bringing them home and have so much fun with them that I don't like to object."

My suggestion was not to try to force a liking for snakes—but merely to try to understand them. Snakes are probably the victims of more erroneous beliefs than any other group of animals. Some popular misconceptions, and the true facts about them, are:

1. *False:* All kinds of snakes are venomous. *True:* Most snakes are harmless.

2. *False:* A snake thrusts out its tongue as an act of hostility. *True:* A snake uses its tongue as a sensory organ to explore its surroundings.

3. *False:* Snakes have no fear of people and are constantly on the lookout for victims. *True:* Most snakes do not display an aggressive disposition toward people; if possible, they creep away and hide at a human's approach.

4. *False:* Snakes can sting as well as bite. *True:* No snake can inflict a sting.

5. *False:* Snakes have great hypnotic powers. *True:* Only the snake's unblinking stare, caused by its lack of movable eyelids, gives us the idea that it is trying to hypnotize its victim.

6. *False:* Snakes spring from the ground to attack a victim. *True:* No snake jumps clear of the ground to strike.

7. *False:* Snakes are slimy. *True:* Snakes are completely covered with dry scales.

8. *False:* Snakes have yellow blood or no blood at all. *True:* Their blood is red and practically the same as that of a mammal.

When you get to know the truth about snakes, and understand why they behave as they do, you may find yourself regarding them with interest rather than horror.

Reptiles—Past and Present

Snakes are reptiles, a name scientists have given to a group of animals that includes lizards, turtles, crocodiles, and alligators. The name was suggested by the Latin word for "creeping".

Reptiles were the most important animals on earth millions of years ago. Porpoise-like species lived in the ocean while batlike reptiles flew in the air. The land was dominated by reptiles called dinosaurs. At first they were no larger than rabbits; later they developed species far bigger and heavier than the largest elephant. We do not know for certain why these mighty creatures disappeared—changes in the earth's climate may have been the cause. Whatever the reason, the importance of reptiles dwindled and warm-blooded mammals became the outstanding animals.

THE COLD-BLOODED SNAKES

All reptiles are alike in being covered with scales or bony plates, and all are cold-blooded. (They derive their heat from external sources, whereas warm-blooded animals derive theirs from within their bodies.) We find, however, that reptiles vary greatly in the way they live and in the places they inhabit. Many of them dwell only in regions where summer conditions prevail throughout the year; but there are some snakes that have to adjust to a climate with extreme variations of heat and cold.

Sleeping Through the Winter. Though cold does not endanger a snake's life until it reaches a few degrees below freezing, a smaller drop in temperature is enough to cause sluggishness; and a sluggish snake does not have the energy to procure food. The solution in cold climates is to hibernate in a well-sheltered rocky crevice or in the ground below the frost-line. In this way the snake is protected from a fall in body temperature that would be low enough to cause death. The animal can survive hibernation without eating, provided it is in a healthy and well-fattened condition at the beginning of its long rest.

THE SNAKE'S BODY—MORE THAN A TAIL

Many children, and countless adults as well, think of a snake as a long tail attached to a head. This is far from a true picture—there is a very efficient body between head and tail!

This body contains a stomach capable of amazing distension and digestive powers, a liver, kidneys, and other organs, too. The snake's heart differs from a mammal's in having only three chambers. (A mammal's heart has four.) The right lung is quite elongated, much more developed than the left.

THE SNAKE'S TAIL

The length of the tail differs according to the species. However, if you scrutinize a snake's underside, you will see that the tail has a definite starting point. There a distinctly enlarged scale—sometimes divided into two overlapping parts—covers the orifice through which wastes pass. This marks the beginning of the tail.

Another way of distinguishing the tail from the rest of the body in most snakes is that the underside scales are large and each of them extends across the whole undersurface of the body—whereas the scales on the underside of the tail are almost always arranged in two columns. A zoologist dissecting a snake observes a still more obvious division of tail and body, for the long series of ribs ends where the ribless tail begins.

THE SNAKE'S HEAD

There are two reasons for the snake's fixed gaze: it has no movable eyelids, and its eyeballs are capable of only slight motion. This results in its "stony stare" and the false belief that snakes hypnotize their prey.

The Snake's Hearing Aid. Though snakes have no ears, they might be said to have a sense of hearing as sounds are transmitted to them through ground vibrations. Tests have been made with cobras to illustrate this point. After the snakes' eyes had been bound with adhesive tape, someone walked toward the animals. Immediately they reared and faced in the direction from which the footsteps were approaching. By way of contrast, the noise made by blowing a bugle brought no response.

This inability to hear sounds carried through the air tends to disprove the Hindu snake charmer's claim that music charms serpents into dancing. The truth seems to be that the snakes merely follow the continuous movement of the musician's arms or knees as he plays his reed instrument.

You can quite easily see the snake's nostrils. There is one on either side of the snout, and they function in the normal manner.

MOULTING—HOW SNAKES SHED THEIR SKIN

Your child may be thrilled by the discovery of a discarded snakeskin in the course of his summer wanderings. If he visits the zoo he may see just how this moulting takes place. The snake loses its lustrous appearance before shedding; its bright colours are dimmed. Even the eyes become milky and the colour of the eyes is obscured.

This goes on for a week or two; then the snake's normal coloration returns and it is ready to moult. It finds a rough, hard object and rubs its nose and chin against it until its skin breaks. Once the head is freed, the snake wriggles its body until the whole skin peels off, inside out.

Why Shedding is Necessary. Moulting is necessary because the skin to which a snake's scales are attached cannot grow. After the skin has stretched as much as possible to accommodate the growing snake it must be discarded. Actually a new layer of skin forms beneath the old one before moulting takes place. There is no regular interval for shedding: it depends to a great extent on the age and vitality of the reptile. Young snakes shed more frequently than adults, and healthy individuals more often than those in poor condition.

How Snakes Move

If you discover a snake on hard-packed soil, you will notice that it moves very slowly, But once it gets off this smooth surface into long grass or on rough ground, it will whisk out of sight with surprising swiftness.

Observe a captive snake and you will see the reason for this change in pace. When it is placed on a large piece of glass, it will slip and slide ineffectively; but if it is transferred to loose sand, it is immediately able to make progress. This it does with sideways movements, keeping the full length of its body against the ground.

You will observe that the creature leaves in its wake a series of slightly curved piles of sand; these prove to be pivots the reptile has raised in pushing its body forward. Next watch a snake on rough grass. Here it will travel with even greater ease—each blade of grass serves as a pivot.

"Legs" Without Feet. To produce this undulating movement—apparently its most usual method of travelling—the snake depends largely on its muscles and ribs which, in effect, are footless legs. The ribs are attached to the backbone and also to the muscles and the slightly overlapping scales on the under-part of the body.

When the muscles are moved forward, the scales are carried forward also. When the muscles are pulled back, the lower edges of the scales press and catch against any roughness on the surface over which the snake rests, and push it forward, using the rough spot for leverage. The snake does not move muscles all along its body at the same time; instead, it brings them forward gradually, and the scales move in waves.

Side-winding. Another method snakes occasionally employ is to curve the body into an S form and then straighten it out again, pushing forward a little in the process. Some desert snakes have developed a specialized method called "side-winding" which is practically

SIDEWINDING FOR DESERT TRAVEL

Most snakes move forward with the body flat against the ground. Not so this desert rattler, which progresses in S-shaped loops—a motion known as sidewinding. This is an effective technique for moving on sand and it is used not only by the American rattler, but by snakes in the deserts of Africa and Asia as well.

indescribable except that the body is thrown into great loops and seems to be flowing sidewise. Using these motions a snake does not waste energy building pivots; yet it does not slip backward.

Snake Tracks. Snakes leave trails in sand or dust that are just as revealing in their way as mammal footprints. Experts not only identify the kind of snake by its trail—they can tell the approximate rate of speed at which it was moving when the trail was made.

How Snakes Breed

It is often said that some snakes lay eggs while others bear living young; yet actually all species reproduce by means of eggs. The difference between egg-laying and "live-bearing" consists in this: the live-bearing female retains the eggs in her oviduct *until the embryo is fully developed.* When the offspring are "born" they are covered by a thin membrane which soon bursts. Only about one-fourth of the known species of snakes follow this procedure.

SNAKE EGGS

When a female of the other species is ready to deposit her eggs, she finds a sunny sandbank or rotting log in which to burrow a hole.

There she lays her eggs—the number, size, and shape depend on the species. Usually they are elliptical, with flattened ends. When first laid, the eggs are covered with a moist and sticky skin which gradually becomes tough and leathery. They absorb water and thus continue to grow after leaving the mother's body until they have increased about one-third in size.

THE EGG-TOOTH

Projecting from the middle of the upper jaw of the full-grown embryo is an egg-tooth with which it slits the tough egg-skin when it is ready to emerge as a perfectly formed young snake. If you rub your finger over the nose of a baby snake you may feel this egg-tooth, which remains until the baby is about a week old.

How Snakes Kill

It may well be that the horror snakes arouse in many people is evoked by their methods of killing. A tiger's prey is just as dead as a snake's victim; but constriction and poison somehow seem more sinister means of inflicting death than fang and claw.

Snakes get their food in three different ways. For the first and most primitive, the reptile seizes its prey by throwing its coils about a victim —without constriction—and then swallows it alive. Constriction is a second method, suffocating the victim until its heart and lungs can no longer function properly. At one time it was believed that constrictors crushed the bones of any creature within their grip; today we know this theory to be erroneous.

Poison is the third method of killing. There are several types of poisonous snakes; those known as vipers and pit vipers have the most effective poison apparatus. The group includes rattlesnakes, copperheads, water moccasins, bushmasters, and the tropical fer-de-lance.

HOW POISON FANGS WORK

All these snakes have hollow fangs in the upper jaw, firmly anchored to the bone above, which they can move to thrust the fangs forward for a strike. When they are not in use, the fangs can be folded back against the roof of the mouth.

As a child, you may have been told that the mere pressure of a snake's fangs against a solid substance brought forth the venom. It is not quite so simple as that. The snake has its poison supply in two sacs—one in either cheek. Each sac is connected to the fangs by a duct that runs under the eye and over the bone to which the fangs are attached. When the viper strikes, muscles that surround the poison sacs contract and force the venom through the ducts into the fangs, from which it flows to the wound just made in the victim's flesh.

HEARTY EATERS

The ability of snakes to swallow objects larger than themselves is one of their most spectacular traits. The larger snakes, such as pythons and boas, sometimes devour a goat or small deer whole. Such a feat would be impossible without a number of special body features with which Nature has provided them.

Let's look at their jaws, for example. An extra bone hinges the upper jaw to the lower, allowing them to spread far apart. Also, the lower jawbones are held together only by elastic ligaments and they can separate at the chin to increase the size of the mouth further. The teeth point backward and thus present no obstacle to objects taken into the mouth. Even the snake's sides are adapted to the task —they have great elasticity and can stretch to many times their normal dimensions!

THE MOVABLE WINDPIPE

Despite all these helps, you might still expect a snake to choke to death in trying to swallow anything large enough to force its jawbones wide apart. The snake overcomes this difficulty by being able to extend a portion of its windpipe forward—even a few inches beyond its open mouth if need be! By this means it can breathe during the long slow process of forcing down a meal apparently far too big for its size.

Some species of snakes can live on three or four big meals a year; others may eat a moderate meal every week or ten days.

The Ways of a Rattler

Children are understandably curious about the hows and whys of a rattler's rattle. How does a tail tip turn into a rattle? Why do some snakes have rattles? How does the rattle work?

The rattle is made up of a series of horny sections or "buttons" on the end of the spinal column. They are loosely interlocked, and when the snake vibrates its tail they click against each other. Many other kinds of snakes also vibrate their tails, and if they happen to be lying among dead leaves the resulting rustle sounds like a rattle. However, the rattlesnake's vibration is distinctive. It is a half metallic, half insect-like sound, somewhat like the dull buzz of the bumblebee.

THE RATTLE RINGS

At birth a rattler has a bulbous swelling at the tip of its tail. When the snake moults, the tip of its old skin cannot be pulled over this enlargement, so it remains and forms the beginning of a rattle. As successive moults take place, the tip of the skin that cannot be shed forms an additional segment or ring. The rings form around a bone known as the "shaker", made up of the last seven or eight vertebrae which fuse together soon after the snake is born.

The old theory that a ring is added each year has been disproved. Sometimes several moults take place in a year and rings are added; it is also possible for the snake to moult without a new ring being created. This irregularity, not to mention the fact that rings are often broken from the end, makes it impossible to reckon a snake's age by the size of its rattle. If a rattle is unbroken, however, you may approximate the animal's age by allowing one year for each two rings.

WHAT THE RATTLE IS FOR

Many snakes have the habit of vibrating the tip of the tail when they are excited, but the rattler is the only kind equipped with a "noise-maker". We do not entirely understand the purpose of the rattle. The once general belief that this reptile always rattles before striking is no longer credited. Apparently it does use its rattle, as a rule, to try to frighten enemies dangerous to its own safety.

As for the theory of "warning" prospective prey, some observers have decided that this snake sounds its rattle to startle birds, rabbits, or other possible victims into momentary inactivity, thus gaining time for a strike. Other people claim that it never rattles before attacking. There are many reports of rattlers that never rattled at any time, and habitually struck without warning.

KINDS OF RATTLESNAKES

There are no less than fifteen different species of rattlesnakes in the United States and they live in many localities. The deadly diamond-back of the south-eastern states frequents neighbourhoods where water is plentiful, the timber rattler lives in woodland mountain regions, the prairie rattler haunts the Great Plains of the West; another species is found in desert wastes.

Rattlers are among the more important kinds of snakes in the United States that bear live young. The mother gives her offspring no care—but none is necessary. They are able to fend for themselves immediately, and have been seen eating ten minutes after birth!

Spectacular Deadly Snakes

A visit to the snake house at a zoo gives you a first-hand acquaintance with species you would never welcome as house pets, though they are well thought of by zoo keepers.

THE GOOD-NATURED BOA

One of these deadly creatures is the boa constrictor—a big reptile of South America that reaches a length of eighteen feet. It is quite hardy in captivity, and many specimens are good-natured and easily fed with birds and small mammals. Though most South American Indians dread this boa and believe it to be poisonous, it is not. As a rule this boa seems anxious to keep away from humans, but it will occasionally appear in a native village, apparently attracted by the domestic fowl.

Still greater in size than the boa constrictor is a water boa known as the anaconda, native to the river valleys of northern South America. Reliable records show that this species sometimes attains a length of twenty-eight feet. The anaconda is the largest snake in the New World.

PYTHONS—THE LARGEST SNAKES

Among the most fearsome-looking reptiles in a zoo are the pythons, which have been imported from Asia or Africa. There are giants among them: a twenty-five-foot Indian python may weigh more than two hundred pounds; the reticulated python, not quite so thick in body, may be nearly thirty feet long. The large pythons eat a variety of animals, but their taste runs to fairly large mammals.

"Snake-charming" showmen frequently use relatively small specimens of the rock python in their acts, as these snakes become very docile in captivity. Nevertheless, there is always some danger. If the snake accidentally throws a complete coil about the body of the performer, it will begin to constrict and throw new coils. The "charmer" must quickly straighten out the reptile or be in real danger of strangulation. Anyone who closely watches a snake charmer with a python or boa, will observe that every movement of his hands and arms is made solely to prevent the snake from forming a coil.

THE COBRA'S DOUBLE PERSONALITY

A child who has been reading colourful stories of the Orient in which cobras play a sinister part, may well be disappointed when he sees this snake in the zoo. When it is not excited, this dangerously venomous reptile looks quite commonplace. Alarmed or angry, the cobra presents a far different picture, weaving its raised head back and forth with its hood erect.

The Cobra's Terrifying Hood. The hood is actually only the skin of the neck stretched taut. The cobra has a series of ribs on the sides of the vertebrae of the neck, and when it is excited it uses powerful muscles to draw these ribs forward, thus stretching its skin and forcing the scales wide apart.

Seen from the back when its hood is spread, the Indian cobra gives the impression of having eyes on top of its head. But what the observer sees are merely markings; the eyes are at the sides of the head, little of which is visible when the hood is open. It is a mistake to think that cobras can be identified by the erection of the hood; other snakes—such as the harmless hognose snake—possess the same ability.

While people most frequently think of India as the home of cobras, these snakes also dwell in Africa. The king cobra, which may grow as long as eighteen feet, is the largest venomous snake known. It is very aggressive and its poison is deadly. The common Indian cobra, which rarely attains a length of more than six feet, also causes many deaths every year.

Three British Snakes

THE GRASS SNAKE

The grass snake (*Natrix natrix helvetica*) is the commonest snake in England and Wales, but it does not occur in Scotland except perhaps in the Border counties. In Ireland there are no snakes at all, and fable has it that Saint Patrick drove them all out of the country.

It is difficult to describe the colour of the grass snake accurately, as there is so much individual variation, and scarcely any two specimens look alike. Generally speaking, it is greyish on its upper side, tinted with green or brown, and it has two rows of dark spots running from head to tail. Underneath it is a mixture of grey and white, with a yellowish throat. Behind its head it has a distinct "collar" of yellow or orange—hence the name of "ringed snake" by which it is sometimes known. The presence of the collar will at once distinguish the grass snake from the viper.

The length of a grass snake varies according to the sex, the females being longer than the males. Some females may measure four feet in a large specimen, whereas males seldom grow much longer than two feet, though in exceptional cases they may reach three.

The grass snake is not confined to any one particular habitat. It is found in hedgerows, particularly if the undergrowth is well developed, in fairly open woodland, or on heaths. It has a strong liking for water, and is a good swimmer, so that it may be found in water-meadows and beside streams.

The grass snake is not poisonous, and, though it may "strike" at a person who handles it, there is no harmful intent, for it usually keeps its mouth closed. As a means of defence, however, it can discharge an evil-smelling liquid from its hinder end.

The food of the grass snake is varied. It is very fond of frogs, and

THE HARMLESS GRASS SNAKE

This is the commonest snake in England and Wales, though in Scotland it is found only in the Border counties. Apart from the two rows of dark spots, it is greyish with green or brown tints, and grey and white underneath. It is harmless to man.

will also take the common toad, as well as newts, tadpoles and fish, which it catches in the water. It will also steal young birds out of the nest, sometimes climbing to a considerable height to do so, and young mice and voles are eaten, though it will not tackle an adult.

When feeding, the grass snake grasps its prey by any convenient part of its anatomy and swallows it whole. Being non-poisonous, it cannot kill its prey with a venomous bite as many poisonous snakes do, and it does not constrict the victim either. Although provided with teeth, these are merely used to hold the victim while it is being swallowed; snakes never chew their food, as their teeth are not adapted for this operation.

The grass snake will lay its eggs in any place where there is warmth and humidity—heaps of grass or manure, sawdust and so on. The number of eggs varies from six to forty or so. The eggs usually take eight weeks to hatch.

In the autumn grass snakes begin their hibernation, choosing a sheltered place like a hole in a wall, beneath a pile of stones, or even in an old rabbit burrow. They come out of hibernation again in early spring.

THE BEAUTIFUL SMOOTH SNAKE

The smooth snake (*Coronella austriaca*) is a beautiful creature, and

THE SMOOTH SNAKE IS RARELY SEEN

Scales so smooth that they hardly show give this snake its name. It is usually grey, though it
may be brown or even red, and has dark spots down its back. It lives chiefly on heathland in
Dorset, Hampshire and West Surrey, and usually hibernates in a sandy bank.

one that responds well to being kept as a pet. It is, however, a rare
snake, found only on heathland in Dorset, Hampshire and West Surrey.
Its usual colour is grey, though some specimens may be brown or even
coppery red. It has dark spots down its back, while underneath it is
grey or brown, sometimes mixed with pale yellow or white. Its scales
are so smooth that they hardly show.

The smooth snake is quite small, seldom measuring more than two
feet long; the females are larger than the males.

The food of the smooth snake consists mainly of lizards, though it
also eats very young mice, shrews and voles. Like the grass snake, it
is non-poisonous, but it does slightly constrict its prey before
swallowing it.

Little is known with certainty about the breeding of the smooth
snake, but probably mating occurs very early in spring, though the
young are not actually hatched until August or even September.
Litters vary in number from four to fourteen or more.

The smooth snake goes into hibernation a little later than the grass
snake. The usual place for hibernation is a hole under some roots
or in the side of a sandy bank, but old mouse holes are frequently used.

The Viper is Poisonous

The viper or adder (*Vipera berus*), our third British snake, is our only venomous species. It occurs freely in England, Wales and Scotland, in very varied country. Heaths, moors and woodlands are its main habitats, but the viper is also to be met with in hedgerows and sometimes on downland.

WHAT THE VIPER LOOKS LIKE

It is important to be able to recognize a viper, as its bite can be dangerous. Its colour is very variable, but it has a dark zig-zag line running down its back, and its head is broad, with golden eyes and a dark mark which looks rather like a "V" on top. The best way to recognize a viper, however, is by its short, stumpy tail, which is quite unlike that of the grass snake or the smooth snake. It is a relatively short snake, females usually measuring no more than two feet, and males a little shorter than that.

The poison of the viper is produced by a pair of glands in its upper

BRITAIN'S ONLY POISONOUS SNAKE

The adder or viper, found in England, Wales and Scotland, as well as other European countries, has a zig-zag line running down its back, and is rarely more than two feet long. It lives on heaths and moorland, or in woods, but may be met with in other places. Its bite is rarely fatal to man, but necessitates urgent treatment.

jaw, and when it bites the poison is forced out of the glands and along channels that connect with the fangs. Though seldom fatal, the bite of a viper is most unpleasant, and can be dangerous. The snake will not attack man if unprovoked, but anyone stumbling on one accidentally, as for instance in long grass, will probably be bitten. Medical help should be sought at once.

The viper feeds on lizards, field mice and voles. The prey is first bitten, and then, when killed or at least rendered passive by the poison, it is swallowed whole.

Adders mate in April or May, after an elaborate courtship ceremony. The young are born alive in August or September. Like all our other reptiles, vipers hibernate during the winter months.

WHEN YOU ENCOUNTER A SNAKE

If you accidentally come upon a snake and are frightened, just bear in mind that the snake is doubtless as anxious to get away from you as you are to avoid it. Remember that it has no "power of hypnotism". This has been proved many times by experiments in which birds, guinea pigs, and other animals were placed in cages with a snake and where they acted entirely unconcerned about their reptile companion. If you can think of a snake as "just another animal", it will be easy for you to remain calm and move away from your unwelcome discovery.

If you are actively interested in snake collecting, you ought to be thoroughly familiar with first-aid treatment for poisonous snakebite and have a snakebite kit with you on all field trips if there are vipers in the vicinity.

You will also want to have a "snake stick" for capturing live specimens. A two-pronged metal fork attached to a pole, or a cut stick with a forked end, may serve your purpose. You can pin down the snake behind the head until you are ready to pick it up and transfer it to a bag.

Snakes as Pets

When a youngster has captured a harmless snake, such as a grass snake, and wishes to keep it as a pet, he may want to build a cage especially for his prize. It is important that the cage should not be too small, or the snake will be restricted in its movements, and so will be very uncomfortable in captivity. The cage should be at least equal in length to the reptile's body. This will make it possible for the snake to coil and uncoil and move about comfortably.

A cage should have a water dish large enough for the snake to crawl into. A big ash tray is convenient and large enough for a small snake. Cover the floor of the cage with moss, gravel, or slightly moistened sand to make cleaning easier. The cage should be wiped out regularly with warm water and soap, and the floor covering changed. All waste matter and uneaten food must be removed daily.

There is no harm in exposing a snake to direct sunlight provided that shade is available at all times. Sun that does not feel excessively hot to your hand may be dangerously hot for a snake; a reptile's body absorbs heat and becomes warmer and warmer, as would a piece of iron lying in the sun. A rock or block of wood placed in the cage helps to provide shade, and it is also useful to the snake for rubbing against when it sheds its skin.

Proper Diet for a Pet Snake. A captive snake that has eaten well from spring and through the autumn may safely go through several winter months without eating. But if you have a local specimen that refuses food for nine or ten weeks during warm weather, it is best to give it its freedom. Forcible feeding by an inexperienced person is sure to be fatal to the snake.

Of course it is necessary to know which snakes eat what. If your snake is one that you have captured yourself it will probably be a grass snake. In that case it will feed on frogs, newts and tadpoles, small fish, or young mice. It will take dead mice if the skin is nicked so that the snake can smell what is inside. If you have bought your snake from a pet shop the shopkeeper will tell you what to feed it on. If in any doubt, ask him.

You may be told that snakes will not touch dead animals, but zoo keepers have found that these reptiles will consume dead prey as readily as living victims. The keepers sometimes teach them to eat raw meat by first serving it mixed with chopped earthworms, then gradually reducing the quantity of worms. When dead food is used, it is moved right in front of the snake to attract its attention.

Captive snakes are likely to be frightened by sudden movements of your hand. "Slow and easy" is the best rule in dealing with them. When you lift a snake, give its long, slender body adequate support; the animal is not comfortable when it is dangled by the head or the tail.

If snakes capture your family's imagination, a generally satisfactory programme is to try keeping one or two during the summer and then to release them so that they may hibernate under natural conditions in wintertime.

Tortoises and Turtles

Of all reptile pets, tortoises are probably the most commonly enjoyed. Your child is apt to bring home a small tortoise that he has bought in a local pet shop.

Unfortunately, thousands of tortoises are entrusted to the care of people who understand little about their way of life. If your child has a tortoise, you and he will certainly want to know more about it. And even if you don't have a tortoise pet, you will agree that it is a fascinating animal to watch and study if you are at all interested in Nature's ways.

ARMOUR PLATE FOR DEFENCE

At first glance a tortoise may give the impression of an inanimate piece of armour; when it is uncertain of its surroundings, it cautiously keeps every bit of its body under its hard shell. Once the tortoise feels safe, however, you will see the snakelike head project from the front of its shell, the pointed tail poke out from the rear, and two wide legs appear at each side. Then you will notice that even the soft body is covered with rough, coarse skin and often with many scales.

You can appreciate the effectiveness of this protective covering when you realize that tortoises have survived for many millions of years with no means of fighting countless larger animals that might attack them. Their success is strictly due to defence equipment. (A noteworthy exception is, of course, the great snapping turtle with its vicious hooked beak.)

There is really very little difference between a tortoise and a turtle.

THE TORTOISE—A POPULAR PET

Tortoises range in size from tiny animals to the giant tortoises of the Galápagos Islands.
The tortoise has armour to protect it from its foes, but if you keep one as a pet in Britain
you will need to look after its health very carefully.

A turtle is an aquatic tortoise—or, if you prefer it, a tortoise is a land
turtle. The name "turtle" is usually kept for marine animals; a fresh-
water tortoise is known as a terrapin.

The Protective Shell. The upper shell (the "carapace") varies in
shape according to the species of tortoise. This shell grows attached to
the tortoise's backbone; in a few species the carapace is quite flat,
in others it is rounded.

The lower shell (the "plastron") also varies in shape and size and
is attached to the breastbone. There is also a great deal of variation
from one species to another as to size and colour of the tortoise's body.
Other oddities include the tail of the snapping turtle, which bears a
saw-toothed armour of plates, and the front and rear "trap doors"
which the Carolina box terrapin can pull up against the carapace to
enclose the body completely!

A child may wonder how a creature encased so completely can
manage to breathe. The tortoise's shoulder and hip bones do most
of the work in contracting and expanding the lungs. The constant

pulsation you can observe in the throat is caused by air being swallowed.

SIGHT, SMELL AND TEETH

Like snakes, tortoises and turtles lack movable eyelids. However, they have a protective membrane which comes up from the lower edge to cover the eye. Some species have nostrils no larger than pinholes, and their poor sense of smell is not surprising. Others, better equipped, have a keen sense of smell.

Though a tortoise has no teeth, its mouth has saw-like cutting edges. It does not bother to chew food but simply tears it to pieces.

HOW TO TAKE CARE OF TORTOISE PETS

Small tortoises are good pet material because they are hardy and easy to feed. The kind you are most likely to find in pet shops is the Mediterranean spur-thighed tortoise (*Testudo graeca*), which is pale ochre with black markings.

Keeping a Tortoise Pet Comfortable. Many people just let a tortoise run wild in their garden, but this is unwise, for it may do considerable damage to plants, since it is a vegetable feeder. Also, a tortoise may dig its way under a garden fence and set off to look for a mate. Tortoises love company, and so it is best to get two, a male and a female. Do not expect them to breed in captivity, however, for they very seldom do, though the female may lay eggs.

It is far better to give the tortoise an enclosure. A section of a flower bed will do nicely; it should contain a few flowering shrubs and some stones, and a good plan is to build in the centre a small rockery that the tortoise can climb. Surround the enclosure with wire netting, which should be buried in the ground to prevent the tortoise from digging under it and escaping. When a tortoise digs under an obstruction it always starts close up to it, so that if the wire netting is turned inwards for about six inches underground, the tortoise will be frustrated. Tortoises are poor climbers, so that the netting need not rise more than six inches or so into the air, but the top edge should also be turned in just in case the tortoise uses the mesh as a ladder;

when it gets to the overhanging portion of the wire it will fall back again.

Hibernation. Like all reptiles in this country, tortoises hibernate for the winter, so provision should be made for this. During hibernation it stops eating, respiration becomes so slow that it seems to have stopped, and the animal becomes perfectly motionless.

As the weather becomes colder in the autumn the tortoise will gradually lose its appetite and become more and more sluggish, usually keeping to one place in its enclosure. Then, if left to itself, it will burrow into the ground under the shelter of a bush and prepare to sleep for the winter.

Many people let their tortoises pass the winter out of doors, but this is a risky thing to do. Apart from the possibility of the winter being more than usually severe—though this would probably not do the tortoise any harm—there is always the possibility of an exceptionally mild winter day tempting the tortoise to come out of hibernation too soon. Unless he were to get back into his warm place before the next frost came, he would certainly die. It is therefore better to provide a hibernation box. As soon as the tortoise shows signs of going into hibernation, it is removed from its enclosure and placed in a wooden box lined with straw, a few air-holes being drilled in the lid. The box can then be stored in an *unheated* shed or garage for the winter. *Never* store the tortoise in a heated room, as this will lead to partial hibernation, and the tortoise will starve. Early in spring the tortoise should be examined every day to see if it shows signs of waking. When it wakes up, give it a drink of water before you feed it, and then put it back in its enclosure.

Feeding a tortoise presents no difficulty. Its chief food is green stuff, such as cabbage and lettuce leaves, dandelions and the like; it also likes tomatoes and fruit, as well as bread, and a drink of milk from time to time is welcome.

Your tortoise should be provided with a shelter for bad weather, as tortoises are susceptible to damp. A wooden box with a hole cut in one side is suitable; it should be raised off the ground to prevent damp seeping in, and a ramp should be provided to enable the tortoise to get in and out easily.

Tortoise Ailments and Remedies. Tortoises are often afflicted with a softening of the shell. This is due to lack of calcium in the diet, and can usually be cured by feeding it with finely-chopped lettuce leaves sprinkled with powdered cuttle-fish. It should be dosed with vitamins to encourage shell formation; a little orange juice and cod liver oil given once a day will supply the vitamins that are needed.

If your tortoise develops running eyes in conjunction with laboured breathing and a discharge from the mouth, it has caught a cold. There is a danger of it developing pneumonia, so treatment should be given at once.

Put the tortoise into a closed space with a bowl of hot water with a few drops of friar's balsam in it, covering the bowl with wire gauze to prevent the tortoise from falling into the water. Leave it for thirty minutes, and repeat the treatment four times a day until the breathing is easier. Then keep the tortoise indoors in a warm place for a week,

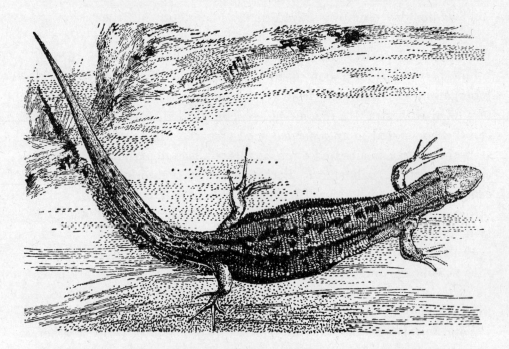

THE COMMON LIZARD

The number of different species of lizards is very great, and there are vast differences between those that live in various parts of the world. Here is the Common or Viviparous Lizard, which of course gives birth to its young alive, though many lizards lay eggs. It lives in Britain and other European countries.

by which time it should be well enough to return to its enclosure in the garden.

Shell-rot, caused by a bacterium, sometimes affects tortoises, appearing as small holes in the plastron which gradually set up a decay. It will kill the tortoise unless treated. Paint the holes with iodine, and then plug them with a mixture of zinc oxide and oil of cloves.

After hibernation, your tortoise's eyes may be covered with a bluish film, due to the presence of a piece of grit, or some other foreign body. The best cure is to bathe the eyes with a weak boracic solution. If the eyelids are stuck together after hibernation they can be freed by bathing them with lukewarm boracic.

Our British Lizards

We have three British species of lizards, though one of them, the slow-worm, looks like a snake and is often mistaken for one, as it is without legs.

THE COMMON LIZARD

The common lizard (*Lacerta vivipara*) is widely distributed over England, Wales and Scotland, and is the only reptile native to Ireland. It is found everywhere, usually in dry places, though it also inhabits marshes as long as there is dry ground near by.

The colour of the common lizard is extremely variable. The back is usually some shade of brown, varying from dark brown to light, but may occasionally be greyish or even greenish. Underneath it is usually orange in males and yellow in females, with a sprinkling of small black spots. It grows up to seven inches long, the female being longer than the male.

The common lizard feeds on insects and spiders, and also on worms. It is quick and active in catching its prey, dashing in and seizing it before it has a chance to get away.

Mating time for the common lizard is from the beginning of April to the end of May. At mating time the males fight fiercely for possession of the females. The specific name *vivipara* means that the young are born alive. The young can catch their own food almost immediately after birth, and their mother soon leaves them to fend for themselves.

THE SAND LIZARD

The sand lizard (*Lacerta agilis*) is the rarest of our three lizards. It is larger than the common lizard, growing up to eight inches in length, and the sexes differ somewhat in colour. The female is greyish brown or brown on top, with a darker stripe down the centre of her back; she has brown spots with white centres distributed over her back, and underneath she is usually cream. The male is much greener than the female, especially during the breeding season.

The sand lizard is confined to sandy districts, especially in Dorset and the New Forest. Its food is generally similar to that of the common lizard. It does not have living young, but lays eggs in a hole in the sand.

THE SLOW-WORM

The slow-worm (*Anguis fragilis*) is often mistaken for a snake, but it is really a lizard without legs. The female is bronze with a darker stripe down her back, while the male is grey or greyish brown.

Slow-worms are found in woodlands, heaths and sandy districts at the seaside. They are distributed throughout England, Wales and most of Scotland.

The slow-worm eats earthworms, insect larvae and spiders. Its favourite food, however, is slugs. In spite of its name, it is active in seizing its prey, and its appetite is voracious.

The young of the slow-worm are born alive, in a gelatinous envelope.